Group Sol[illegible]s

Cooperative Logic Activities

Grades K–4

Skills

Visual Discrimination, Counting, Sorting, Classifying, Using Process of Elimination, Using Deductive Reasoning, Communicating, Sequencing, Spatial Visualization, Recognizing Shapes and Colors, Using Fifty and Hundred Charts, Comparing Amounts, Map Reading, Finding Locations on Maps, Using Map Legends

Concepts

Numeration, Computation (Fractions), Directionality, Ordinal Numbers, Money, Mapping

Science Themes

Patterns of Change, Models & Simulations, Systems & Interactions, Stability, Structure, Scale

Mathematics Strands

Number, Measurement, Geometry, Pattern, Functions, Statistics and Probability, Logic, Algebra

Nature of Science and Mathematics

Cooperative Efforts, Real-Life Applications

by

Jan M. Goodman

GEMS
Great Explorations in Math and Science
Lawrence Hall of Science
University of California at Berkeley

What Are Group Solutions?

These activities are designed for groups of four students. Each student receives a clue about a problem and needs to share that information with all the other group members in order to reach the correct solution. The entire group is responsible for finding the solution, and it can ONLY be figured out by connecting the information from ALL the clues. **The essential element of *Group Solutions* is that the students must work together—cooperatively and logically—to figure out the solution.**

In addition to its strong emphasis on cooperation, *Group Solutions* fosters the development of many key skills and concepts in mathematics and other subject areas. The lively interactions and sense of achievement lead to student questions such as "Are we really doing math?" and "Can we do this again, soon?"

This book includes more than fifty cooperative logic activities organized into five categories, or "Families" (Searches, Bear Line-Ups, Secret Number, Coin Count, and Maps). Introductory sections explain how to use the book; discuss cooperative learning and logic in the classroom; and provide guidelines for classroom management and effective handling of problems that may arise.

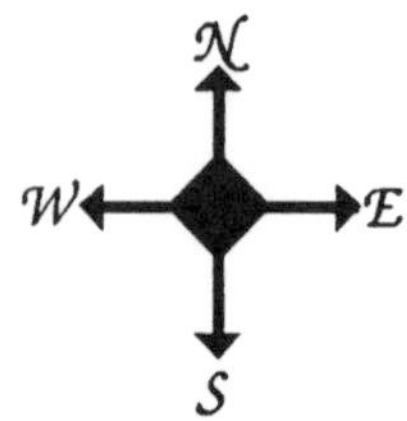

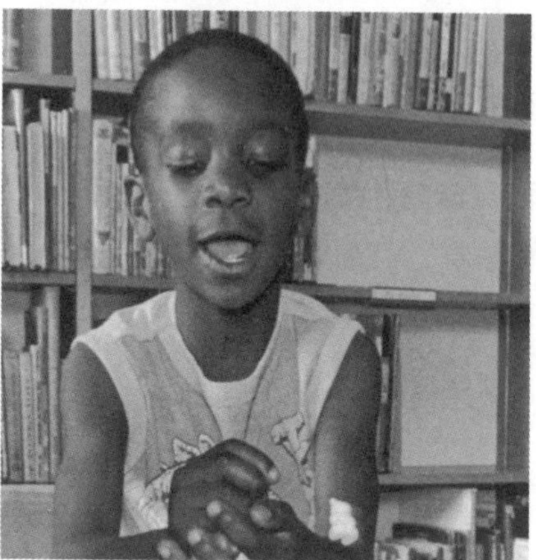

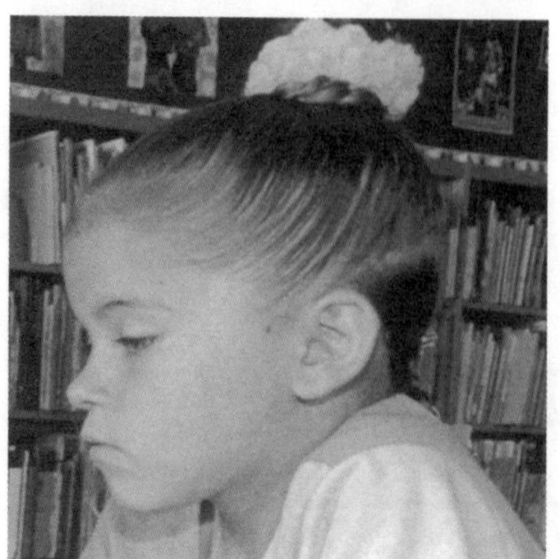

CONTENTS

Illustrations
Jan M. Goodman created, designed, and produced all the student clue cards, manipulatives, and related illustrations in this guide. Drawings on pages 33 and 35 by Lisa Klofkorn.
Cover design by Carol Bevilacqua and Lisa Klofkorn.

Photographs
Richard Hoyt

Publication of Group Solutions was made possible by a grant from the McDonnell Douglas Foundation and the McDonnell Douglas Employees Community Fund.

The GEMS project and the Lawrence Hall of Science greatly appreciate this support.

Initial support for the origination and publication of the GEMS series was provided by the A.W. Mellon Foundation and the Carnegie Corporation of New York. GEMS has also received support from the McDonnell-Douglas Foundation and the McDonnell-Douglas Employees Community Fund, the Hewlett Packard Foundation, and the people at Chevron USA. GEMS also gratefully acknowledges the contribution of word processing equipment from Apple Computer, Inc. This support does not imply responsibility for statements or views expressed in publications of the GEMS program. Under a grant from the National Science Foundation, GEMS Leader's Workshops have been held across the country. For further information on GEMS leadership opportunities, or to receive a publication brochure and the *GEMS Network News*, please contact GEMS at the address and phone number below.

International Standard Book Number: 0-924886-48-X

Comments Welcome

Great Explorations in Math and Science (GEMS) is an ongoing curriculum development project. GEMS guides are revised periodically, to incorporate teacher comments and new approaches. We welcome your criticisms, suggestions, helpful hints, and any anecdotes about your experience presenting GEMS activities. Your suggestions will be reviewed each time a GEMS guide is revised. Please send your comments to:

GEMS Revisions
Lawrence Hall of Science
University of California
Berkeley, CA 94720.

On the web: www.lhs.berkeley.edu/GEMS

Our phone number is (510) 642-7771.

Great Explorations in Math and Science (GEMS) Program

The Lawrence Hall of Science (LHS) is a public science center on the University of California at Berkeley campus. LHS offers a full program of activities for the public, including workshops and classes, exhibits, films, lectures, and special events. LHS is also a center for teacher education and curriculum research and development.

Over the years, LHS staff have developed a multitude of activities, assembly programs, classes, and interactive exhibits. These programs have proven to be successful at the Hall and should be useful to schools, other science centers, museums, and community groups. A number of these guided-discovery activities have been published under the Great Explorations in Math and Science (GEMS) title, after an extensive refinement process that includes classroom testing of trial versions, modifications to ensure the use of easy-to-obtain materials, and carefully written and edited step-by-step instructions and background information to allow presentation by teachers without special background in mathematics or science.

Staff

Principal Investigator
Glenn T. Seaborg

Director
Jacqueline Barber

Curriculum Specialist
Cary Sneider

Staff Development Specialists
Katharine Barrett, John Erickson, Jaine Kopp, Kimi Hosoume, Laura Lowell, Linda Lipner, Laura Tucker, Carolyn Willard

Mathematics Consultant
Jan M. Goodman

Administrative Coordinator
Cynthia Ashley

Distribution Coordinator
Gabriela Solomon

Art Director
Lisa Haderlie Baker

Designers
Carol Bevilacqua and Lisa Klofkorn

Principal Editor
Lincoln Bergman

Senior Editor
Carl Babcock

Contributing Authors

Jacqueline Barber
Katharine Barrett
Lincoln Bergman
Jaine Kopp
Linda Lipner
Laura Lowell
Linda De Lucchi
Jean Echols
Jan M. Goodman
Alan Gould
Kimi Hosoume
Sue Jagoda
Larry Malone
Cary I. Sneider
Jennifer Meux White
Carolyn Willard

Acknowledgments

True to the philosophy of *Group Solutions*, this book was a collaborative effort. The author wishes to thank the following:

The *EQUALS* program at the Lawrence Hall of Science, whose publication, *Get It Together*, inspired the activities in this guide.

Jaine Kopp, friend and co-worker, who helped develop and refine many of the activities and was always willing to interrupt her own projects to edit the book, often on a moment's notice.

Lincoln Bergman and *Carolyn Willard*, dependable and talented re-write editors.

Carl Babcock, whose editing and desktop publishing skills enhanced this guide's readability and beauty.

Jacquey Barber and *Linda Lipner*, who provided ideas, vision and clarity throughout the guide's development process.

Beverly Braxton, *Celia Cuomo* and *Phil Gonsalves*, office colleagues who consistently offered support and wisdom when asked if activities and graphics needed adjustment.

Laura Clark and *Grace Coates*, for their insightful contributions to the section on "Cooperative Logic in Multilingual Classrooms."

Cynthia Ashley, who efficiently coordinated the numerous administrative details for the local and national trial tests.

Nancy Kedzierski, who facilitated the construction of thousands of cooperative logic envelopes and distribution of bears, coins and cubes for our trial kits; and the other GEMS staff members who helped with the lengthy process.

Carolyn Adams, *Jan Baumbach*, *Diane Meltzer*, *Mary Pino*, *Becky O'Rourke* and *Gayle Stevens* whose students eagerly participated in our photographic sessions.

Marianne Camp, who helped to analyze huge amounts of data from the local trial tests and offered continuous encouragement and enthusiasm for the project.

Sheila Khalov, my life partner, who never complained when, instead of meaningful conversation and lively games after dinner, we entertained friends and relatives with "Find the Pizza" and other cooperative logic activities.

The *local and national trial test teachers* who were willing to delve into cooperative logic and provide valuable feedback to help improve this guide.

And, especially, the *students* who proved that young children could work together cooperatively and productively.

Reviewers

We would like to thank the following educators who reviewed, tested, or coordinated the reviewing of this series of GEMS materials in manuscript and draft form. Their critical comments and recommendations, based on presentation of these activities in classrooms nationwide, contributed significantly to these GEMS publications. Their participation in the review process does not necessarily imply endorsement of the GEMS program or responsibility for statements or views expressed in these publications. Their role is an invaluable one, and their feedback is carefully recorded and integrated as appropriate into the publications. Thank You!

ALASKA

Coordinator: Cynthia Dolmas Curran

Iditarod Elementary, Wasilla
Mary Helen Cole
Cynthia Dolmas Curran
Michael J. Curran
Jana Schlereth DePriest
Ruth Felberg
Deborah Waisanen

CALIFORNIA

GEMS Center, Huntington Beach
Coordinator: Susan Spoeneman

Circle View Elementary School, Huntington Beach
Mary R. Berrier
Stan Carroll
Alice R. French
Anita Fuller
Marilyn Wilton
Amy Yoshihara

William E. Kettler Elementary School, Huntington Beach
JoAnne Smith Berg
Kay Fletcher
Patricia Gates
Elaine Goodnoe
Sandy Harrell

San Francisco Bay Area
Coordinator: Cynthia Ashley

Edison Elementary School, Alameda
Jane Baldi
Barbara Klaasen
Sandra Downey

Foothill Elementary School, Pittsburg
Gary Diaz, Coordinator
Gail Caruso
Gisele Cassidy-Phillips
Iris Contreras
Annie H. Clawson
Susan M. Luoni
Fran Marshack
David Rose
Sol Rosenshein
Nadine Seedall

Franklin Elementary School, Berkeley
Katherine Lunine
Scott Wachenheim
Mario Zelaya

Glassbrook Elementary School, Hayward
Marianne Camp
Laura Suzanne Clark
Patricia Anne Geary
Marina Xavier

Lincoln Elementary School, Newark
Linda Agler
Midge Fuller
Beverly Hall
Judy Levenson

Los Medanos Elementary School, Pittsburg
Sandi Dias
Cheryl Duran
Paula McNally
Mary Pino
Linda Switzer

Martin Luther King Jr. Junior High School, Berkeley
Phoebe Tanner

Oxford Elementary School, Berkeley
Joseph Brulenski
Carole Bennett Simmons
Janet Levenson
Kathy Rashidi

Park Day School, Oakland
Karen Corzan
Catharine Keyes
Susan McLean
Joan Wright-Albertini

Peralta Year Round Elementary School, Oakland
Elizabeth A. Bandy
Paulette Besse
M. Anne Larsen

Sierra School, El Cerrito
Laurie Chandler
Gail Gundelach
Phil Gilsenan
Harry Lackritz Gray
Janie Havemeyer

Washington Elementary School, Berkeley
Carolyn R. Adams
Rita Davies
Diane Meltzer
Patricia Ungern

GEORGIA

Coordinator: Yonnie Carol Pope

Mountain View Elementary, Marietta
Robin M. DeVaux
Cathy Howell
Ruth Lang
Diane Pine Miller
Samantha Marie Miller
Yonnie Carol Pope
Barbara Smoot
Denise Langston Thomas
Kimberly L. West

KENTUCKY

Coordinator: Dee Moore

St. Joseph School, Louisville
Kathy Fensterer
Diane Flechler
Mary Jane Mascarich
Barbara Smoot
Theresa Watson

Simpsonville Elementary School, Louisville
Sheryl Block
Brenda Breidert
Elizabeth C. Brown
Paula Smith

TEXAS

Coordinators: Melanie Lewis and Sarah Fogg

Deep Wood Elementary School, Round Rock
Kathy Culpepper
Lana Culver
Carol Hernandez
Sandra Mouldin
Marilyn F. Sutch
Julia Swain
Sherry Wilkison

WASHINGTON

Coordinator: Scott Stowell

Bemiss Elementary School, Spokane
Cindy Beard
Brenda Fuglevand
Shelly Fuller
Margaret A. Haines
Patricia Moen

Longfellow Elementary School, Spokane
Joy Chastek
Birgit Gorman
Cris Welch
Sandra Westerman

Foreword to the Fourth Edition

Group Solutions for the 21st Century

Group Solutions was first published in 1992, in response to requests from elementary school teachers who wanted to involve their students in cooperative logic mathematics activities. At the time, we had no idea how popular the book would become or the impact it would have on educators, parents, and children. As we developed and tested the activities, we saw the delight and concentration on children's faces as they worked together to solve what they viewed as engaging "math puzzles," but we could never have imagined that the publishing of the guide would have dramatic results like the following!

- *Group Solutions* quickly became a top seller in the GEMS series and has stayed there. The book consistently appears on the "Top Three" list of GEMS guides.

- Over 50,000 copies of *Group Solutions* have been sold, nationally and internationally. It has been widely distributed throughout the United States, as well as in Mexico, Canada, Spain, England, Sweden, Singapore, Taiwan, Japan, Turkey, and South Africa.

- *Group Solutions* was featured in the teacher bonus section of Scholastic's Trumpet Book Club.

- A complete *Group Solutions* classroom kit, produced by Sargent Welch (1-800-727-4368), under exclusive agreement with GEMS, is now available to teachers for immediate use in their classrooms.

- A sequel entitled *Group Solutions, Too!*, published in 1997, has also been enthusiastically welcomed by teachers and students and received a Parents' Guide to Children's Media award.

Why has this book become such an important tool for elementary school teachers? After eight years in circulation, these are among the most frequent responses:

***Group Solutions* teaches more than mathematics.** Its enormous popularity is a testimony to the fact that educators want our students to develop as autonomous thinkers and creative problem solvers who are able to use multiple intelligences to construct and share mathematical knowledge. The activities, while centered on important mathematical concepts, go far beyond basic problem solving. In the age of standards-based learning, *Group Solutions* has become a tool to address mathematical content within the context of building a community of learners who value their own knowledge and are able to learn from their classmates. The book helps students think critically and collectively. When children's minds are opened up and they recognize their own potential, they are better able to access the curriculum standards.

The two *Group Solutions* guides have been used to introduce, reinforce, and broaden students' understanding in mathematics in cognitive curriculum content areas, including numerical relationships, computation, geometry, discrete mathematics, functions, and logic. At the same time, a compelling strength of *Group Solutions* is in the realm of social development and group dynamics. The cooperative logic activities help students become contributing members of a group of collective thinkers, and thus prepare them for the real-life world of cooperative problem-solving experiences that occur every day in the workplace. Rarely are there times when adults are asked to solve problems in isolation, with no help or support from outside sources. Yet, far too often in school settings, this is exactly what is expected of students.

***Group Solutions* helps prepare students for the future.** When leaders of the Fortune 500 companies were asked to name the qualities and skills they most valued in their employees, teamwork was their number one priority, followed by these characteristics, in order of importance— problem solving, interpersonal skills, oral communication, listening, creative thinking, and leadership (from *Creativity in Action*, Creative Educational Foundation, 1990). *Group Solutions* helps prepare students for today's classrooms, tomorrow's work world, and a future where cooperation and interdependence are essential for global survival.

When three second-grade students patiently encourage an emerging reader to decode the clue on her card, even though there are group members who can read fluently, they're learning **teamwork**.

When a shy third grader timidly suggests a new method to set up the "bear line-up," and the group values her risk-taking and invites her to rearrange the bears, they are able to **listen** and **problem solve**.

When a fifth grader who is perceived as "smart" acknowledges that his solution does not work and accepts the input of a classmate, this builds **interpersonal skills**.

As kindergartners and first graders animatedly discuss which monkey fits all four clues, this demonstrates **oral communication** and **creative thinking**.

Finally, when students of all grades recognize that "four heads are better than one," opportunities for authentic **leadership** abound.

***Group Solutions* empowers students and teachers.** When the guide was first published, there was some controversy as to whether children in elementary schools are developmentally able to participate in cooperative problem solving activities. For example, do the children simply follow teachers' directions and go through the motions to share clues and come up with a solution, or do they actually participate in interactive reasoning and teamwork? As an elementary school principal and classroom teacher, I have seen *Group Solutions* used with diverse groups of students in a range of learning environments, and my answer to this question is unequivocally "YES!" Time after time, I've watched students develop important skills that are essential to cooperative learning, provided that the teacher clearly communicates her expectation that they can work things out themselves and allows them the time and space to do so. If left to their own resources in a supportive setting, even the youngest children will figure out a way to successfully negotiate group process issues and solve the problem. In a supportive and empowering setting, the innate compassion, cooperation, and humanity in children can be mobilized through *Group Solutions* activities.

***Group Solutions* offers teachers unique opportunities for assessment of students.** Traditional textbook and standardized tests provide a one-time measure of students in light of a prescribed set of skills and concepts.

Since *Group Solutions* requires children to take charge of their own learning, teachers are free to observe, document, and evaluate student progress in less conventional but equally important areas of the curriculum. Teachers can gain insight into each student's problem-solving strategies, reasoning processes, and self-esteem. Observation over time reveals answers to a multitude of questions, for example:

- What are the child's strengths and needs as a problem-solver?
- Does the child look at the whole picture first, or use parts to lead to the whole?
- Which of the multiple intelligences are most useful to each child as a problem-solver? For example, does she have strength in logical-mathematical, spatial reasoning, or interpersonal areas?
- How does each child use the math manipulatives to help solve the problems?
- How is the student perceived by group members? What is her/his level of confidence?
- How open is the child to other points of view?
- What issues arise most commonly in groups? What discussions need to occur within the classroom community to address these challenges?

After eight years in circulation, *Group Solutions* has survived the test of time and remains a vital and viable tool to teach and apply mathematical concepts and build classroom community. In the face of a strong movement towards standards-based education where there are well-defined content criteria for learning, it is heartening to see that teachers continue to use curriculum that will help develop well-rounded children. The kindergartners featured on the cover of *Group Solutions* have now finished middle school, and other children in the photographs will likely have graduated high school and moved on to careers or further training and education. It is my deepest hope that the skills and confidence they gained through cooperative problem solving will in some way help them to face the challenges of today's complex world.

—Jan M. Goodman • Oakland, California • June, 2000

➤ An Introductory Scenario ◄

It is math time in your classroom and the topic is cooperative logic.

The students are working in small groups. Each group is trying to solve a problem. An assortment of coins is spread out on the desks. The room is noisy, but it is productive noise and the children are having fun. There is a lot of discussion, as students share their clues and exchange ideas.

In one group, students are reading their clues. "I think we should start with my clue first," Rosa says.

"My clue says there are no half dollars, so we can get rid of a lot of coins!" Robert interrupts. "My clue says all the coins are silver, so there must be no pennies."

Irma adds, "We better save my clue for last, because it says there are two more dimes than nickels, and we don't know how many nickels OR dimes we have. Does someone have a clue about nickels?"

Another group has developed a system for sharing clues.

"I went first last time so now I'll go last," says Malcolm, checking the list he has made of group members. "It's your turn, Jessie. But on the next problem, you go last."

One group believes they have solved the problem. They wave their hands excitedly to get your attention.

"We did it!" they proclaim. You look at their solution. You ask the group how they know that they are correct.

"We read our clues again and everything fit," they reply, in unison. Each student proudly reads her clue, and verifies the solution.

"Do you want to try another problem?" you ask.

One student says, "Yeah! Get the hardest possible one!"

Another student cautions, "Maybe we should build up to the hardest one." You agree, and send the materials person for the next problem in the sequence.

You move towards another group. They are having a heated discussion.

"Manny, stop grabbing the coins!" shouts Laura. "You are messing everything up! Now there are seven pennies and my clue says there is an even number of each coin." You remain near the group but resist the desire to intervene.

After several moments of coin shuffling, Maria says, "We better start over again. This time, you can only touch the coins when it is your turn to read the clue." Manny and Laura stop bickering and the group focuses again.

"I know what we're supposed to do," directs John, as he moves the entire pile of coins to his side of the table. "Give me your clue, Sarah."

Sarah, remembering a basic cooperative logic rule, shyly mumbles, "No. We're supposed to keep our own clues."

Simon agrees, "I have a clue too."

John is impatient. He pushes the coins to the center of the table. "Go ahead and read the clues," he sighs. "But it's going to take longer this way!"

In Ms. S's first grade class, the students are also working with coins and cooperative logic. Each group of four children has a plastic cup, an assortment of pennies and four clue cards. The students are directed to put the pennies in the cup as they read their clues. As the eight groups of children work together, Ms. S moves from table to table, observing and offering positive comments about cooperation. She pauses a short distance from Michelle's group and watches a conflict in progress.

Michelle has left the group. She's thrown her clue card on the table and has moved her chair to a nearby desk. She sits in the chair, mumbling and sulking while Keisha, Juan and Andrew continue to solve the problem. Keisha is concerned about her friend and looks over at her, but Michelle makes a face in disgust. Ms. S does not intervene, though she is tempted to do so. Michelle stays in her seat while the group solves the problem and each student glues down 14 pennies to record the solution.

When the activity is complete, Ms. S convenes the students for a group meeting. She asks, "How many groups feel that they worked well together?" Seven of eight groups raise their hands enthusiastically. Michelle's group does not.

"What did you do to work together?" she asks the class. The children respond:

"We didn't grab the cards."

"We shared the money and the clues."

"We listened to each other. We didn't yell. We talked it out."

Ms. S turns to Michelle's group, and inquires, "Michelle, did your group work well together?"

"No," Michelle says adamantly. The other group members nod in agreement.

"What happened?" Ms. S asks.

"They were mean," Michelle complains. "They didn't share the pennies. The money was all on Keisha's desk and I couldn't reach it."

"What did you do?" Ms. S continues.

"I got mad. I gave them my clue and went away," Michelle admits.

"What else could you have done?" Ms. S probes.

"I could have told them I couldn't reach the pennies. I could have asked them to move them closer," says Michelle.

"What could the group have done?" Ms. S asks.

"I knew Michelle was mad," says Keisha. "I could have given her some of the pennies. I was going to move them but there was a hole in the middle of our desks and I was afraid they'd fall on the floor. "

"Do you think you could work better together next time?" Ms. S asks.

The entire group agrees. They decide to stay in from recess and solve the problem again. When the class returns from their break, Ms. S provides time for Michelle's group to report their success.

It is math time in your classroom and the topic is cooperative logic. With practice, all students are involved. All students feel successful. All students recognize that they are valuable members of their group and of their classroom. As facilitator, you are removed from the traditional role of teacher and are able to move from group to group, gaining academic and social insights about your students.

Group Solutions will challenge both your students and your patience. With practice, your students will learn to work together in a group to solve a common problem. They will gain a skill that will help them succeed as children and adults in the workplace. As students build vocabulary, learn to think logically and apply important concepts, they will *consistently* ask, "Are we really doing math? Can we do this again, soon?" The rewards will be tremendous.

➤ How to Use This Book ◄

Overview

This book contains cooperative logic activities that are grouped in five "families"—**Searches, Bear Line-Ups, Secret Number, Coin Count** and **Maps**. The book begins with families that have concrete concepts and materials **(Searches, Bear Line-Ups)**. We suggest you start with these two families to help your students build a solid foundation in cooperative logic. Then, you can proceed to **Secret Number, Coin Count** and **Maps**, which are more complex. Within each family, the activities are presented in order of difficulty. The **Activity Grid** at the back of the book contains suggested **grade levels** for each activity. (See page 147 for how to create a *Group Solutions* kit for your school.)

Materials

The following materials are needed for **all** activities in this book:

- Card stock (optimal paper for durability) or duplicating paper in white and at least one other light color
- Letter size envelopes
- Paper cutter (optimal) or scissors
- Additional manipulatives (not included in guide):
  Coins (real or authentic-looking play money) for **Coin Count**
  Cubes in five colors (wood cubes, unifix or multi-links) for **Cubeville Map**
  Teddy bear counters for **Bear Line-Ups**, **Bear Park** Maps and **Bear Street** Maps

NOTE: If you do not have bears or cubes in your classroom, the guide includes pages that can be duplicated to use instead of these materials. See Sources For Materials *on page 138 if you wish to purchase bears, cubes or coins.*

Clue Cards

To prepare for an activity with the entire class, you will need to create one cooperative logic envelope for each group of four students. The envelope includes clue cards that are duplicated from *Group Solutions.* There are **four or six clues** on each clue card page. Each clue is labelled with the title of the activity and marked with a **magnifying glass** so students can easily identify it.

For your convenience, each clue card also is marked with either a **four or six box grid** in its upper right hand corner, as illustrated on the next page. The grid indicates the number of clues on the page (the number of boxes) and the position of each clue on the page. The grid is an organizational tool that will help you maintain complete sets of clues, in the event that envelopes and clue cards are interchanged through student use. A complete set of four or six cards will have one clue shaded with a box from each part of the page. The grid is of no significance to students, although they may inquire about it!

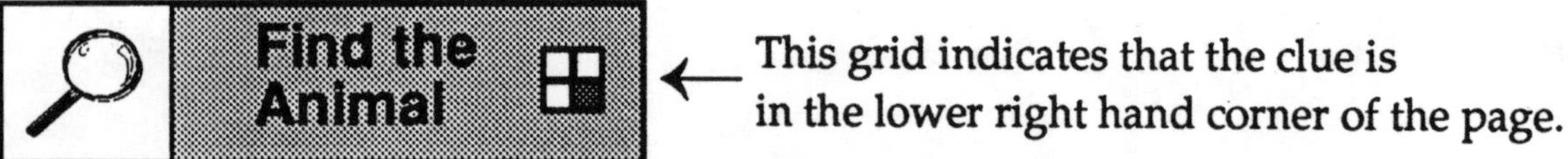

Find the
Animal
This grid indicates that the clue is
in the lower right hand corner of the page.

At the bottom of each clue card page, there are brief **teacher notes**. The notes contain **essential** instructions for the preparation of the cooperative logic envelopes and will help you proceed with the activity. For example, important oral directions for students are listed in the teacher notes for the first several activities in each family.

Step by Step Preparation

1) Read the **introduction** to the family and notes for teachers on each clue card page.
2) Duplicate the clue card pages on card stock or paper. You may wish to laminate the clues for increased durability.
3) Cut the cards on the dotted lines. There should be either four or six clue cards for each activity.
4) Place the clue cards in a white envelope. Label the envelope with the title of the activity.
5) Make one envelope for each group who will use the activity.

NOTE: The initial preparation time for this guide is extensive. However, once you have created cooperative logic envelopes, you can re-use them year after year. You can also create a "library" of cooperative logic problems to be shared at your grade level or by the entire school. Parents can be very helpful in the preparation process.

Additional Student Materials

For each activity in the **Search** family, there is one page of picture cards that must be cut up and included in the cooperative logic envelope. Be sure to duplicate the picture cards on paper that is a **different color** than the paper for the clues. The pages of picture cards are identified by the activity's title and a picture of a hand:

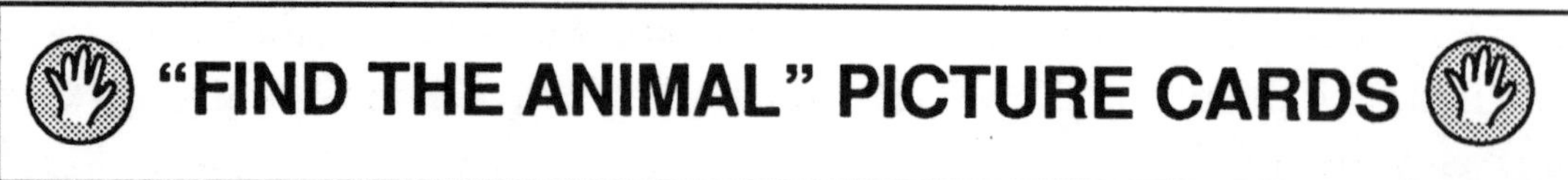

At the end of the **Bear Line-Up** section, there is a page of manipulatives that can be used if you do not have teddy bear counters in your classroom. This page is also suggested for assessment activities in the Bear Line-Up family. Two pages of Bear Line-Up mats for activities 1–6 are also at the end of the section.

The **Secret Number** family includes Fifty and Hundred charts for student use.

Recording sheets that can be used for record-keeping and assessment activities are included in the **Coin Count** section.

For each **Map** activity, there is a map that should be duplicated and distributed with the envelope. The map is used with activities with the same title. For example, the **Bear Park Map** is used with the clues for the eight Bear Park activities. You may wish to laminate the maps so that they are more durable. A grid is also included for use with the Cubeville maps if you do not have wood cubes in your classroom. Enlarged copies of all three maps are provided in the Appendix starting on page 149.

Blank cooperative logic prototypes are included in the Appendix on page 142. Teachers and students can use these pages to create their own cooperative logic problems for the classroom.

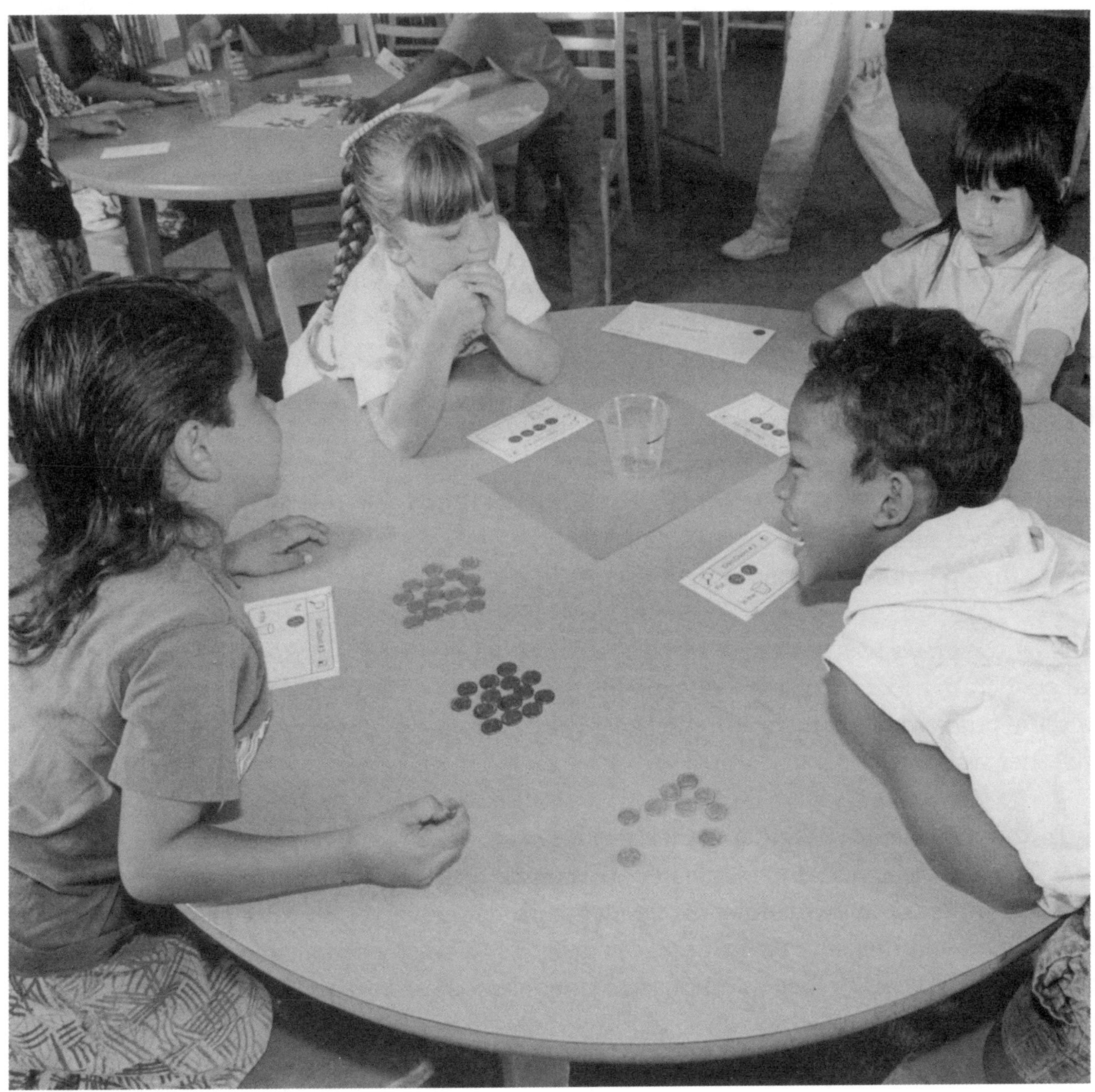

➤ Cooperative Logic in the Classroom ◄

These questions are often asked about cooperative learning and logic. Responses are based on the classroom experiences of teachers who have used this approach extensively with their students.

What is cooperative learning?

Cooperative learning is an increasingly popular form of instruction that has been used in a variety of ways to promote group interaction and collaboration in the classroom. It provides an alternative to the traditional instructional setting where students work individually with little or no communication with peers.

Each teacher's view of cooperative learning is different and closely relates to the individual needs of her students. In most cooperative learning environments, four to six students are grouped randomly or deliberately so they can interact with materials and with classmates as they learn. Peer assistance is highly valued as students work cooperatively. They learn to articulate their reasoning and appreciate diverse approaches to problem solving.

What is cooperative logic?

Cooperative logic is a highly structured form of cooperative learning. It was first featured in the *Green Box* (Humboldt County Schools, Office of Environmental Education, 1986). It was adapted for Grades 4–12 in *Get It Together* (EQUALS, Lawrence Hall of Science, University of California at Berkeley, 1989).

Group Solutions was written in response to numerous teachers who expressed their need for cooperative logic problems for students in Grades K-4. We have modified the format and the process so that it is appropriate for the developmental needs and abilities of younger students.

Through cooperative logic activities, groups of students are given clues and must work together to solve a problem. Each student receives a clue and has the responsibility to share the information with other group members. Ultimately, the entire group is responsible for the solution, and the solution can *only* be reached by connecting the information from all of the clues. When questions and dilemmas arise, students are encouraged to look within the group for answers.

What is the educational value of cooperative logic?

Cooperative logic teaches children to work together, a necessary survival skill in our daily lives and in the workplace. In a non-competitive environment, students develop organizational skills that will be of life-long value as they pursue future careers.

Through cooperative logic, students learn to communicate information and ideas to their classmates.

In order to come up with a group solution, students must learn to listen, to be patient, and to value the contributions of others. Through the process, students learn to appreciate a variety of approaches to a problem.

Cooperative logic is empowering for students. As students learn that they are essential to their group, they gain self-confidence. The focus shifts from teacher to student, as children learn to rely on their peers for answers and evaluation.

The *Group Solutions* activities move beyond the textbook and challenge students to reason, make deductions and form conclusions. In a group, students are able to succeed at higher level thinking tasks that are beyond their capacities as individuals.

What is the teacher's role during the cooperative logic process?

You are essential to the success of cooperative logic. Although you do not provide the solution, you facilitate an environment where students can work together safely and productively. You introduce the activities, structure the groups and help students develop the skills to communicate with their peers.

Your role is to closely monitor the progress and dynamics of each group. You intervene only when it is clear that the group needs outside support. You assist when necessary but you do not provide the solution to the cooperative logic problem. However, feel free to pose questions that will lead to the solution!

As facilitator, you can work with students to brainstorm and record a list of ways they can work together to solve the problem. Discuss how an observer would know if a group were cooperative (heads are together, one person speaks at a time; voices are polite; materials are shared).

The role of facilitator requires a great deal of patience on your part. In order for students to work out their own social issues, they are likely to experience some discomfort and tension in their groups. We recognize that it is difficult to watch students struggle to resolve issues. However, students gain tremendous confidence and personal power when they realize that they can work through problems together, without outside intervention.

Can young children really work together cooperatively?

Children will take part in, learn from, and relate to the group problem-solving experiences in *Group Solutions* in a variety of ways, relative to their age, level of development, and prior experience. As a teacher, you have a good sense of what is reasonable to expect from your class. If your students have not had much experience with cooperative learning, it is unlikely that they will immediately understand every task or sail smoothly through the interactive processes to arrive at a group solution.

It is safe to assume that most students will have difficulty as they learn to cooperate, work together, share, clarify a problem, and communicate information. Older students may be able to comprehend the general task more readily and can also be expected to reflect upon and apply their experiences to other projects. However, all children need to accumulate cooperative and challenging problem-solving experiences. Practice over time will help students build a solid foundation for these essential social and reasoning skills.

NOTE: All Group Solutions activities were tested extensively in classrooms in California and across the nation. Many kindergarten and first grade teachers were initially doubtful that their students would be able to approach and solve these problems harmoniously, successfully, and cooperatively. However, they later told us how pleasantly surprised they were to see the remarkable student growth and strong sense of individual and group accomplishment that resulted from the cooperative logic process.

How do I foster cooperative learning in my classroom?

Team-building activities are wonderful tools to help students begin to work together in small groups. The following open-ended activities will encourage students to find group solutions in less structured settings as well.

Food Sharing

Give each group some food to share, for example, a bowl of popcorn or a small box of raisins. The group's task is to come up with a fair method to share the food with all members. Each group member must understand and be able to explain the sharing process. They all must be satisfied with the way that the food was shared as well. After the food is divided, have groups report on the methods that they used to share.

Construction Crews

Give each group a manipulative material, for example, building blocks, cubes, pattern blocks. Ask them to work together to build one structure or design with the materials. Have students share their work with their classmates. Encourage them to discover similarities and differences among structures and/or designs.

Group Art

Give each group an assortment of art supplies. Ask each group to create one art piece (for example, one house, one mural, one animal) with the materials. Assign one art project to all students so that you can look at the diversity in the results.

Chain Stories

Ask each group to write one story. Each student can add a sentence to the story. Specify the length (for example, each group member will contribute one or two sentences). The stories can be written, dictated or oral. Each group can create one illustration for their story. A reporter can then read the story to the class.

Which families and activities should be used first?

Begin with activities from families with more concrete concepts and materials (**Searches** and **Bear Line-Ups**). You can use the **activity grid** (included on page 140 and in the information for teachers for each family) to determine which activities are most appropriate for your grade level. Select an activity that will be easy for your students to solve, so they can focus on the cooperative logic process. Start slowly, and take the time to process student solutions and social interactions. Once your students gain skills in cooperative learning, you can proceed to more challenging problems.

How do I introduce a particular cooperative logic activity?

Each cooperative logic family includes several pages of **information for teachers.** This information precedes the student activity pages and includes **introductory activities** to help students explore the manipulatives before they are used in a structured situation. The activities also reinforce vocabulary and concepts necessary to solve the problems. They are essential to the success of cooperative logic, particularly with younger students and less fluent readers/speakers.

The information for teachers also includes a section of tips for teachers on **classroom management**. This will provide you with specifics about how to introduce the particular family to your students. Suggestions are provided for specific grade levels.

To help students understand the cooperative logic process, we strongly suggest that you begin each family with a problem for the **entire class** to solve. Select an activity in the family that will be easy for your students to grasp conceptually (for example, **Find The Animal**). Distribute the animal picture cards to each group. Give one clue to each group. The remaining groups can work without a card, or can have duplicates of the clues. Have the groups present their clues, one at a time. After each clue is presented, ask students to regroup or arrange their animal cards to fit the clue. (For example, if the clue says that the animal has one tail, students should remove the animal with no tail). After all clues are read, compare the solutions for each group to check that they are the same. Have each student re-read her clue to be sure that all solutions fit all clues. Then, ask these questions:

- "Were you able to solve the problem with only one clue?"
- "What did you need to do to solve the problem?"
- "How did you figure out what to do with the picture cards, bears, coins or cubes?"
- "How did you know that your answer was correct?"

After the students have completed the class problem, give them the same or similar problem (for example, **Find the Pet Shop**) to solve in small groups. Assess the process as an entire class when each group has solved the problem.

When is an appropriate time to do cooperative logic?

Cooperative logic activities can be used at any of the following times:

- to reinforce concepts in mathematics and related areas,
- to teach deductive reasoning, communication and collaboration,
- as an alternative to the textbook,
- as a "sponge" activity (after students are proficient with the process) when a lesson is completed or when there is a small amount of available time before recess or lunch.

You can integrate cooperative logic throughout your mathematics and social studies curriculum. For example, if you plan a unit on money, include **Coin Count** activities. When you begin a study of geography, include activities from **Maps.**

How should students be grouped for cooperative logic?

The activities in this book are designed for groups of f**our students** (although some have six clue cards). If your class does not divide evenly into groups of four, create a few groups of five students. Most of the problems have four clues, so you may need to help students establish how to share the work in their group equitably. The fifth student can be in charge of the manipulatives, be responsible for distribution of clues, or receive a clue when the group proceeds to the next problem. It is helpful to keep groups the same for each family.

Students can be **randomly grouped** in a variety of ways. A deck of cards is particularly useful as a way to group students. If your class has 32 students, place eight sets of cards in four suits (for example, four cards each of the aces through the eights) in a bag. Have students select a card from the bag and form a group with students who have the same number as they have. The cards can also be used to assign roles in the group. (For example, the person with the diamond passes out the cards; the person with the club collects the materials.) Students can also pick number tiles, wood cubes or other manipulative from a bag that contains four of each item. When students are randomly grouped, they learn to work with a variety of people in situations that are not predictable. They become more flexible as they adapt to the various personalities in the group.

Or, you may wish to **select your groups in advance of the lesson**. Some teachers balance their groups to distribute class leaders and independent workers or to create a range of ability and language levels.

Kindergarten and first grade teachers may choose to **group students in pairs** for their cooperative logic activities. Later, they can make the transition to groups of four.

What are the rules for cooperative logic activities?

Establish rules that you feel are appropriate for your students. These may include:

➤You are responsible for the information provided by your clue. You may *read* it to other people in your group, but you must always keep it with you.

➤If you have a question, ask your group first. If no one in your group can answer the questions, you should all raise your hands and an adult will assist you.

➤When you finish a cooperative logic problem, read all your clues again to make sure that your solution is correct.

Older students may develop their own rules for their groups. They may come up with procedures to distribute clues or systems for use of manipulatives.

What can I do to support less fluent readers?

The first several activities in each family (with the exception of **Secret Number**) require **minimal to no reading**. These activities use picture clues, often accompanied by simple words and are accessible to less fluent readers and English as a Second Language students of all grade levels.

For activities that require reading, you may wish to group less fluent readers with children who can assist them. However, each member of the group should still be responsible for a clue. If a clue is read for a child, that child can make conclusions about it. Less fluent students should not be denied an opportunity to contribute to the group. No one should assume that a child who has difficulty with reading will also have difficulty with thinking.

Key vocabulary and concepts for each family are listed in the **information for teachers** at the beginning of each section. Review the necessary vocabulary with the entire class or small groups of students before they work with specific logic problems. Be sure to use the introductory activities for each family. They are designed to reinforce vocabulary and concepts.

For adaptations for students whose primary language is not English, see the section "Cooperative Logic in the Multilingual Classroom" on page 25.

How do I assess the progress of the group and individual students?

With cooperative logic, each student in the group is responsible for the solution. When asked, each member of the group should be able to explain the solution or any part of it.

Specific assessment activities are included in the introductions for each family. It is particularly useful to have students keep a written or pictorial record of their group's process and solution. You may want to construct a *Group Solutions* casebook (see page 145) so that individual students can depict their solutions to various activities.

How can I encourage students to write about their solutions?

Math logs/journals can be used to record student reactions to cooperative logic problems. It is helpful to pose a particular question as a focus for student writing. Possible questions include:

Grades K–2

- ➤ Draw a picture of your group working together.
- ➤ Draw the answer to the problem.
- ➤ To focus on one concept, you can give students journal assignments that relate to the specific family, such as "Draw a picture of a line of five bears." "Draw three pennies and two nickels."

Grades 2–4

- ➤ In what ways did your group work well together? List at least one way your group could improve its cooperativeness?
- ➤ How did you contribute to your group? How did you help the group find the solution?
- ➤ Write or draw the solution to your group's problem. Show the steps you took to reach the answer. Prove that it is correct.

If your students have minimal experience with writing about mathematics, it is helpful to compose a sample journal entry with the entire class. For example, the following entry could describe the solution to **Secret Number A**:

> "First, we crossed out numbers 1 to 20 because the secret number was greater than 20. Then we crossed out 40 to 50 because it was less than 40. We crossed out the odd numbers because you could get to it when you count by 2's. When we counted by 5's, we crossed out all the other numbers except for 30. Then, we checked our clues, and it fit all four of them!"

You may wish to have pairs or groups of students write together. Brainstorming key words and phrases can also help students who are reluctant to write.

How do the students know when they have a correct solution?

Students often ask the teacher if their solution is correct. However, they should first be encouraged to check to see that their solution fits each of their clues. If this is the case, their answer is correct.

> ***NOTE:** The teacher notes on clue card pages will tell you if an activity has multiple solutions. If so, encourage students to find more than one way to solve the problem. Later, you can discuss these multiple solutions in more detail.*

Where is the answer key for *Group Solutions?*

We have intentionally omitted an answer key from *Group Solutions* because students have the tools within their group to check their own answers. One important goal of cooperative logic is for students to learn to depend on themselves and their classmates. However, it may be difficult for you to monitor the progress of multiple groups and activities in a classroom. If this is the case, circulate around the room and ask each group to prove that their solution is correct, orally or in writing. If you need to see if a group is correct "at a glance," you may wish to develop your own answer key for the more complex activities in each family. For example, you or your students can color in the squares on the Cubeville Map to represent the solution to the problem. Then, see if the group's map matches yours. If it does not, ask students to re-read their clues and re-think their solution.

➤ Trouble-shooting ◄

Here are some problems that commonly arise, particularly during the beginning stages of cooperative logic, and some suggestions on how to resolve them.

The students will not cooperate!

Sharing

Work with the class to brainstorm methods to share clues and manipulatives. Ask groups that work well together to share the reasons for their success. Devise specific suggestions, for example, **You may touch the bears only while you share your clue.**

Whose clue is best?

Groups sometimes have difficulty deciding which clues are "most important." Emphasize that every clue is essential to the solution, but that it may be more helpful to start out with a particular clue. Older students can often distinguish between clues that are more easily used first and clues that will be more useful later on in the process.

Patience

Be patient. Many students are unaccustomed to collaborative work. Encourage your students to be patient. Remind them that cooperation is hard work, but well worth the effort. Explain that cooperation is a very useful skill in their families and in the job world.

One student dominates the group; the shyer students sit back

This problem commonly arises when students have minimal experience with cooperative logic. Emphasize that each student in the group makes an **equal** contribution to the solution, and that no clue is more important than another. You may need to intervene and suggest systems that promote equity:

- ➤ Rotate the student who distributes the clues and arranges the manipulatives. This assures that every person in the group will have a chance to be a leader.

- ➤ Arrange the groups so that the more dominant students are in their own group. This will leave space for other students to assume leadership roles in the remaining groups.

- ➤ Select a quieter student to present the group's solution to the class.

The groups finish at different rates

If you wish to maintain a non-competitive environment where students are free to proceed at their own pace, you should expect that groups will finish at different rates. This will not be problematic if you provide students with some of the tasks or projects listed below:

➤ Set up a cooperative logic center in your classroom. Equip the center with several problems from one or two families and necessary manipulatives. When a group completes a problem and checks to be sure the solution fits all clues, allow the students to select a new problem from the center. Each group should select a Materials Person. This person is the **only student** in the group who can leave her seat to get materials from the center. **Be sure that students know that they should have only one logic problem at the table at any given time.** The Materials Person must return the completed problem before she can take a new one.

➤ Ask students to predict whether they will arrive at the same solution if they trade clues or read them in a different order. Then, have them test their hypotheses. You will be surprised at the number of children who have yet to discover that the solution will be the same when the clues are redistributed or sequenced differently!

➤ Allow additional time for students to explore the manipulatives after they complete an activity.

➤ Groups or individuals can record their solutions in pictures or words in a Math Journal. Specific suggestions for assessment are provided in the introductory material for each family.

➤ If appropriate, children can develop their own cooperative logic problems with the new problem prototypes on page 142.

➤ Select a follow-up activity from the Assessment and/or Going Further sections for each family. Provide necessary materials and oral or written directions so that students can make an easy transition from cooperative logic problems to the activity.

Students still look to me to validate the "right" answer

Remind students that they have the tools within their group to check the solution. Have each student read her clue and check to be sure the solution fits the clue. When all clues have been read, ask the group if their solution is correct. This technique will clearly demonstrate that students have solved the problem themselves.

Students arrive at an incorrect solution but are convinced it's correct!

This often occurs when groups rush ahead carelessly so that they will be the first to solve the problem. Or, students may change the information from a previous clue so that they can come up with a solution that fits their clue. For example, one clue may specify that there is a blue bear at the front and the back of the line. The next clue may state that there is a green bear in front of a blue bear. A student could interpret that clue to mean that a green bear is first in line. This will invalidate the information from the previous clue.

To help students become more aware of their own process, encourage them to slow down and take a step-by-step approach. Work with the group to re-read each clue and check students' interpretation of the information. Watch closely as they use manipulatives to represent the information on their cards. Have them check their solution after each clue is read to be sure that it matches all the information that has been revealed. Remind students that cooperation and accuracy are more important than a speedy solution.

> *NOTE: Assistance can also be provided by students or groups who have already solved the problem successfully.*

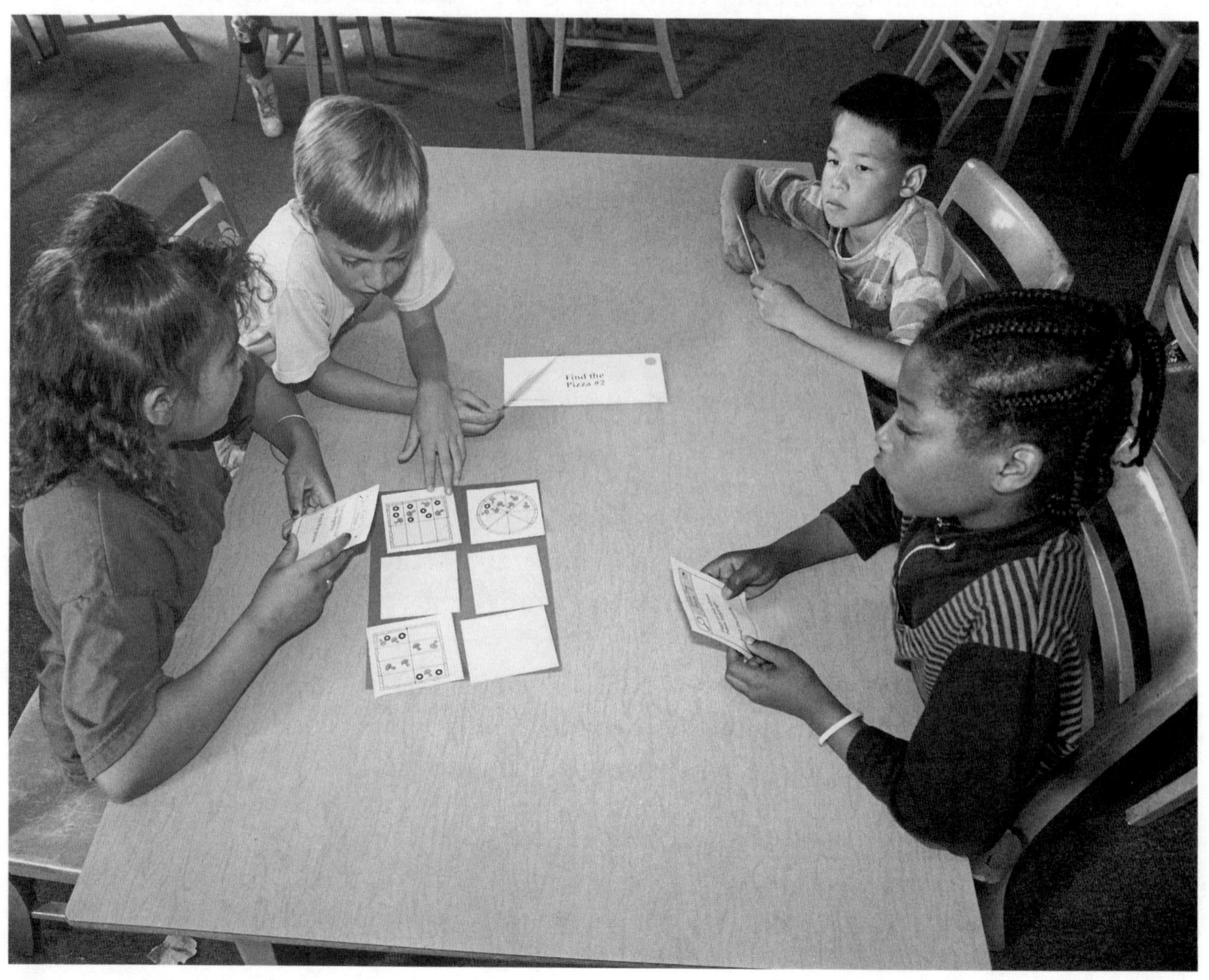

➤ Cooperative Logic in Multilingual Classrooms ◄

by Laura Clark

Group Solutions can be used effectively in multilingual classrooms if the language needs of students are carefully considered. In this section, suggestions are made for **English as a Second Language** (ESL) classrooms, where more than one language is spoken. It also includes adaptations for **bilingual** settings, where instruction is presented in two languages, the children's native language and English.

ESL Classrooms

Group Solutions can be used to facilitate language and concept development in ESL classrooms. The activities combine hands-on manipulatives and cooperative learning opportunities to help ESL students access higher levels of mathematical thinking in their non-native language. For ESL students, consider the following factors:

Vocabulary Development

As students proceed with collaborative problem solving, they will need the vocabulary necessary to understand the clue cards and the concepts that are emphasized in the activities. Children need to learn vocabulary that relates to spatial concepts (for example: near, next to, between, in front of, on top of) and number concepts (for example: more, less, equal, digit, sum, odd, even). This vocabulary is presented in the Overview section of each family. Students will add to this list in a meaningful manner as they encounter the appropriate contexts for using new words. The teacher/facilitator may include other opportunities to support the use of the new vocabulary.

ESL children need concrete experiences related to their own bodies and other physical objects that can be manipulated so that they have a concrete connection to mathematics words that will help solve the problem. Introduce vocabulary in a manner that incorporates a variety of learning modalities with charts, graphics, music, rhymes and movement. If ESL students have extensive experience with the related vocabulary, they will feel less frustrated and more confident in their groups.

Introductory Activities

These activities, featured in the introductory section for each family, are essential for ESL students. Many of the activities merge language with concrete experience to prepare students for independent group work. Try to adapt the activities to reflect cultural and linguistic perspectives.

Social Tension

A certain level of tension is a natural element in cooperative problem solving. Additional social tension will likely arise when a child's ability to communicate is hindered by language differences. Students feel disempowered if they cannot understand the actions of their peers and communicate their own thinking patterns. In order to prevent added tension, you may wish to group limited or non-English proficient students with children who are more fluent in English. However, be sure that all group members keep their own clue cards and everyone has a turn to interact with the manipulatives. If these rules are followed, ESL students will have the opportunity to contribute to the group problem solving process at their own language level, regardless of their fluency in English.

Before the students work in their groups, you may also wish to talk about communication problems that are likely to occur. Older students can observe their interactions as they work together in team building activities and notice what issues arise (for example, some children are less involved; some do not have access to materials). As problems are noted, discuss how the students dealt with communication conflicts. It might be helpful to create a list of student-generated strategies on a sheet of chart paper. This will encourage students to take responsibility for conflict resolution.

Assessment

Assessment for ESL children should focus on the development of their communication skills in relation to their understanding of specific math concepts. **It is important to separate math and language assessment.** Children may have a thorough understanding of the math concept, but may be unable to articulate their understanding with oral or written language. If this is the case, you can observe students' abilities to manipulate materials and contribute to the solution during the group process. Or, you can observe their ability to independently recreate a problem and arrive at a solution with similar materials.

Bilingual Classrooms

In a bilingual setting, *Group Solutions* can be used first to facilitate the development of math concepts in the children's native language and second to facilitate English language development across the curriculum. In accordance with current bilingual theory, new concepts should be introduced in the child's native language so that the child does not have to learn a new concept for which she has no language relationship. As concepts solidify, the transition to English will be easier if you use success-oriented whole group and partner activities from the introductory sections. Assess language development in English and math concept development in the native language.

The first several activities of each family can be solved with little or no reading. These should be ideal for bilingual students. To deal with more advanced concepts in your students' native language, you may wish to translate the clues. The GEMS program is working on a Spanish translation for the student pages of *Group Solutions.*

Laura Clark is a third grade bilingual teacher at Glassbrook School in the Hayward Unified School District, Hayward, California. She used activities from Group Solutions *with her students as part of the GEMS trial test program in fall 1991.*

➤ Literature Connections ◄

There are a great many children's literature books that convey positive lessons relating to cooperation. These books can help set the stage for children to work together on cooperative logic activities. You and your students no doubt have your own favorites. Other books listed here could accompany the activities relating to money, maps, and number. The illustrated version of the classic fairy tale "Goldilocks and the Three Bears" can complement the many activities that include bears.

The books are listed alphabetically by title.

Alexander Who Used to Be Rich Last Sunday

by Judith Viorst; Illustrated by Ray Cruz
Atheneum, New York. 1978
Grades: K–3

Here's a humorous look at how Alexander spends the dollar that his grandparents give him on a Sunday visit. Though Alexander would like to save the money for a walkie-talkie, saving money is hard! He and his money are quickly parted on such items as bubble gum, bets, a snake rental, and a garage sale.

Annabelle Swift, Kindergartner

by Amy Schwartz
Orchard Books, New York. 1988
Grades: K–2

Her older sister's advice notwithstanding, Annabelle's first day in kindergarten is a success. One section ties in beautifully with the Coin Count activity in *Group Solutions* as Annabelle surprises her classmates with her expertise in counting money. This book will especially appeal to kindergarten students, but older students will also enjoy it.

As the Crow Flies

by Gail Hartman; Illustrated by Harvey Stevenson
Bradbury Press, New York. 1991
Grades: Preschool–2

This book povides look at different geographical areas from the perspectives of an eagle, rabbit, crow, horse, and gull. There is a verbal account of each animal's journey followed by an overhead view of the animal's path. The last page includes a big map, a larger context into which each of the smaller maps fits. It is an excellent book to introduce or reinforce mapping skills.

Babushka's Doll

by Patricia Polacco
Simon & Schuster, New York. 1991
Grades: K–3

Natasha is a demanding and rambunctious little girl who receives a doll that turns out to be much more demanding than she is! Natasha is able to get a glimpse of herself through the doll's behavior. This is a good book to start a discussion about cooperative behavior.

Goldilocks and the Three Bears

retold and illustrated by Jan Brett
Dodd, Mead & Company, New York. 1987
Grades: K–3

This classic tale introduces a consistent and predictable scale comparison, with the three bowls of porridge, the three chairs, the three beds, and finally, the three bears themselves. Illustrations in this version include caterpillars changing to butterflies, many varieties of birds' eggs, seeds, and leaves, and forest scenes depicting a system of interacting plants and animals. Here's a fun literary way to spin off from the bears of *Group Solutions.*

How Many Snails?

by Paul Giganti, Jr.; Illustrated by Donald Crews
Greenwillow Books, New York. 1988
Grades: Preschool–3

A young child takes walks to different places and wonders about the amount and variety of things seen on the way, from fish to fire trucks to cupcakes. This book invites the reader to actively participate and count by attributes, as in Searches activities.

It's Mine

by Leo Lionni
Alfred A. Knopf, New York. 1985
Grades: K–2

Three selfish frogs quarrel over who owns their pond and island until a storm makes them value the benefits of sharing. This is a helpful story to use to introduce the merits of cooperation before you begin cooperative activities.

Music, Music For Everyone

by Vera B. Williams
Greenwillow Books, New York. 1984
Grades: K–4

Rosa's grandmother is sick and funds are scarce. Rosa and her three friends all play musical instruments, so they form the Oak Street Band and are paid to entertain at a community gathering. This is a great example of four young girls from diverse cultures working together. This book is part of an excellent series by the same author.

Stone Soup

written and illustrated by Marcia Brown
Charles Scribner's Sons, New York. 1947
Grades: K–3

Three hungry soldiers march into a French village in search of a bit of food. Not until the soldiers begin to make a pot of "stone soup" do the villagers begin to share. Each family contributes a vegetable, meat, grain, milk, or spice to make a soup for the whole village. Though the villagers are tricked into sharing, the benefits of working together are well illustrated.

The Purse

by Kathy Caple
Houghton Mifflin Co. , Boston. 1986
Grades: K–2

Katie keeps her money in a band-aid box until her older sister convinces her to buy a purse. Because she uses all her money for the purse, she has nothing left to put in it! Katie does earn more money and the way she spends it provides a novel twist to the end of the story. This is a fun introduction to the U.S. monetary system.

The Wolf's Chicken Stew

by Keiko Kasza
G.P. Putnam's, New York. 1987
Grades: K–3

A hungry wolf's attempts to fatten a chicken for his stew pot have unexpected results. A delightful book to begin an investigation of 100 as the delectable items the wolf brings to the chicken's doorstep come in quantities related to, or of, 100. When he arrives at the chicken's house to capture her for his stew, he has quite a surprise. The unexpected ending is touching. This book relates to Secret Number activities.

Where the Sidewalk Ends

by Shel Silverstein
Harper & Row, New York. 1974
Grades: Preschool–Adult

This book of poetry delights people of all ages. The poems that involve mathematics in particular are "Smart," "Band-Aids," and "Eighteen Flavors."

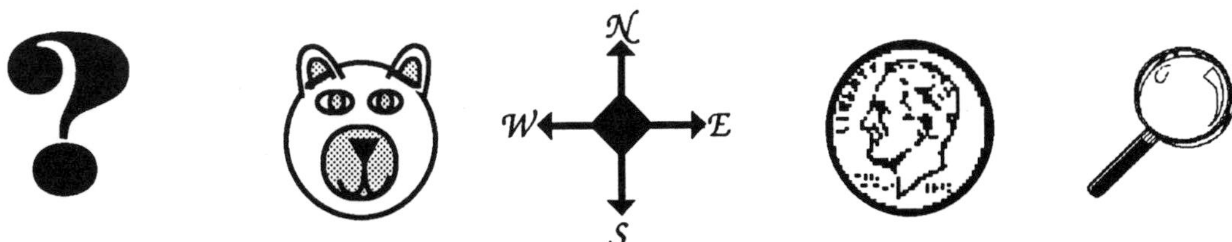

Searches

OVERVIEW

Activities in **SEARCHES** require students to use clues, appealing picture cards, and the process of elimination to locate one object among many! When they open their cooperative logic envelopes, students separate the clue cards (marked with a magnifier) from the picture cards (drawings of houses, animals, monkeys, pet shops, robots, and pizzas). They distribute the four clues and place the picture cards in an area that is easily visible to all group members. Each clue motivates the group to look closely at the picture cards and notice details that are similar and different. After all clues are revealed, only one card remains and the students' search is over. However, they must always check to see that their solution matches all four clues!

Skills

- Visual discrimination
- Counting
- Sorting, classifying
- Use of process of elimination
- Fraction concepts
- Deductive reasoning
- Communication

Concepts and Vocabulary

- Geometry: square, triangle, round
- Numeration: odd, even, more than, twice as many, equally share
- Fractions: half, third, fourth, sixth, eighth

	Suggested Grade Levels					
Activity	K	1	2	3	4	5
Find The House	✓	✓	✓			
Find The Animal	✓	✓	✓			
Find The Monkey	✓	✓	✓			
Find The Pet Shop	✓	✓	✓	✓		
Find The Bear		✓	✓	✓		
Find Rosa's Robot			✓	✓	✓	
Find The Pizza—1			✓	✓	✓	
Find The Pizza—2				✓	✓	
Pizza Match—1 and 2					✓	✓

GETTING READY

Each activity consists of two pages to duplicate—a set of clues and a set of picture cards. Be sure to duplicate the clues on a different color paper than the picture cards. Explain that clue cards are labeled with a magnifying glass; these are the cards to be distributed to individual group members. The picture cards are shared by the group and should be visible to all students.

Place a 9" x 12" piece of colored construction paper in the center of each group's work area. When it is time to distribute cooperative logic envelopes, direct students to place the picture cards on the piece of paper. This will help students share and view the drawings. The color on the paper can also be used to name each group.

> ***OPTION:*** *You may wish to enlarge a set of picture cards or make overhead transparencies so that you can more easily demonstrate the process of elimination for the entire class.*

INTRODUCTORY ACTIVITIES

Stand Up! Sit Down!

This exercise will help students focus on specific physical attributes. Choose a characteristic that is common to many students and direct those students to stand up, for example, "Stand up if you are wearing clothes with buttons to school today." Then, change the attribute: "Stand up if you are wearing something red." At this point, students who have buttons but are not wearing red should sit down. You can also combine attributes for older students, for example, "Stand up if you are wearing pants and have laces in your shoes." Have volunteers choose a particular attribute and direct their classmates to stand up if they fit the category.

Guess My Person

Select five students to stand in the front of the classroom. Try to choose students who have similar attributes. Tell the class that you are thinking about one person and their job is to find that student after you give them some clues. Select a characteristic that will eliminate one or two students, for example, "The person is a girl." Have a volunteer name all the students who fit the category and ask the other students to sit down. Add another characteristic, for example, "The person has brown hair." Continue in this manner until only one student remains. To review the process, ask the class to list the attributes that have been mentioned and check to see that this student has all the characteristics. Older students can choose their own volunteers and select attributes that lead their classmates to guess the person.

Free Exploration

Allow ample time for students to study the picture cards in their envelope before they begin to search for the one card that fits all the clues. Encourage them to discuss the similarities and differences between the cards, for example, "The robots are different shapes. Some have more buttons than others."

TIPS FOR TEACHERS

Grades K–2

It is essential to model the process of elimination with your students, as this process is used to solve all Searches activities. This can be done most successfully if you use an enlarged set of picture cards on full sheets of card stock or drawn on paper. Proceed as described below with an example from **Find The Monkey**.

Give one enlarged animal picture to each of six students in the front of the classroom. Ask the students to hold up the pictures so that their classmates can easily see them.

Choose four students and give each child one clue card. Ask each student to share the clue card, (for example, "a banana") with the entire class. After each clue is read, have students look at the pictures of animals to determine which fit the clue. Ask students to sit down if they have an animal that does not fit the clue. Be sure to ask for specific reasons why the student must sit down, (for example, "their monkey does not have a banana"). Emphasize that once a student sits down because her animal is eliminated, she may not get up again. When all clues are read and only one animal remains, check to see that the picture on the card fits all four clues. Discuss the fact that all four clues were needed to solve the problem and that each was used one at a time. It may also be helpful to suggest that students put the animal pictures in the envelope as they are eliminated by clues.

Grades 3–4

Please note that Pizza Match problems are different from all other **Searches** activities since they do **not** require students to identify one picture that fits all four clues. Rather, it asks them to match four pizzas with four kids. It is important to discuss this change before you proceed with **Pizza Match-1**. You may wish to use the pizza activities as part of a unit on fractions.

ASSESSMENT

Grades K–4

Ask individuals or groups of students to draw a picture that fits all the clues in their envelope. For example, if students have clues for **Find The Animal**, they must draw an animal with one tail, two ears, three legs, and spots. If groups work together on the task, each child can add a feature from a clue card to the animal. As an additional challenge, ask the class to draw a picture that does **not** fit the clues!

Grades 2–4

Have students select a photograph or drawing of a person, place or object from a magazine. Ask them to list all characteristics that describe the picture, for example, "The building is a store. The store has two doors. The store sells tires." When the descriptions are complete, place them in an area near the pictures. Ask students to match each picture with its description.

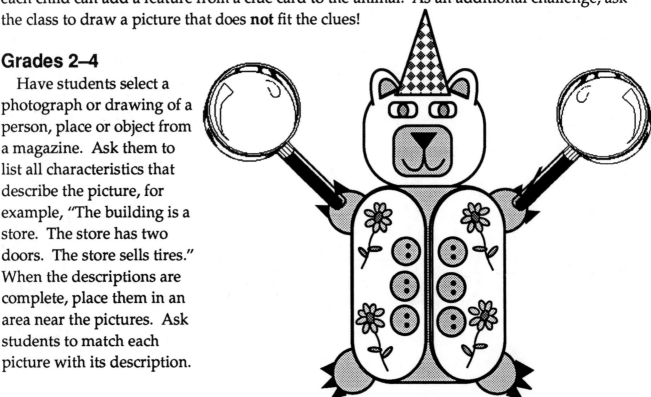

GOING FURTHER

Attribute Train

Tell students that they will line up, one at a time, in a special way. Each student must stand next to a student that has at least one common attribute, (for example, both students have sneakers). Challenge the students to come up with as many different attributes as they can.

Mystery Object

Select an object in the classroom (for example, a red pattern block). Provide the entire class with one clue about the object ("It is red"). Ask two students to find an object that is red. Ask the class to verify whether the object/s chosen fit the clue. Add another clue ("It is made of wood"). Have the two students select an object that fits both clues. Provide additional clues ("It is small. Its shape is a trapezoid.") until the students have found the object. Verify the students' choices throughout the process. For older children, provide the entire description. Ask them to find the object and prove that it fits the clues. When students are familiar with the game, have them work in small groups to select objects and challenge their classmates to find them.

Stuffed Animal Class

Ask students to bring a stuffed animal to school. Use the animals for sorting and classifying. Have small groups of students brainstorm different ways to group the animals, for example: "big/small, long ears/short ears, four legs/two legs." Use large yarn loops or hula hoops to sort the animals into two categories. Older students can create more than two categories and use multiple characteristics, for example, "big animals with spots/big animals with no spots/small animals with spots/small animals with no spots."

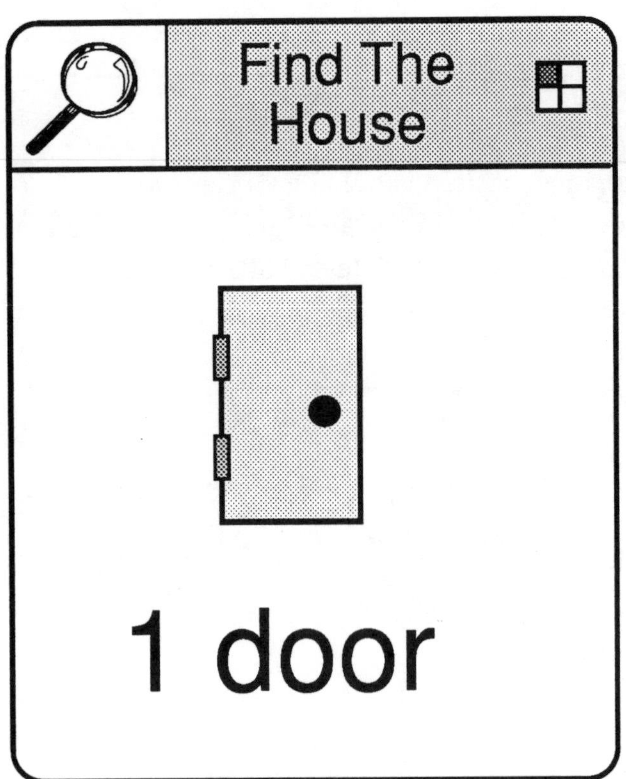

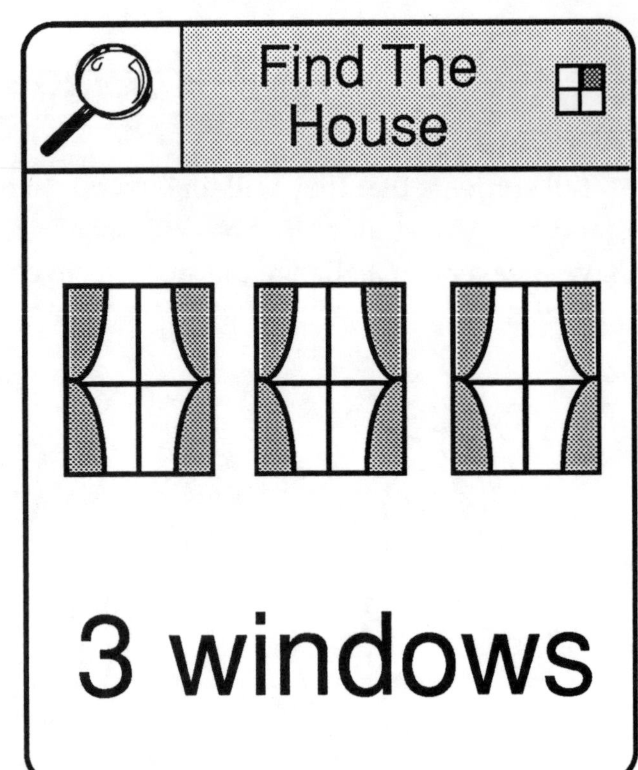

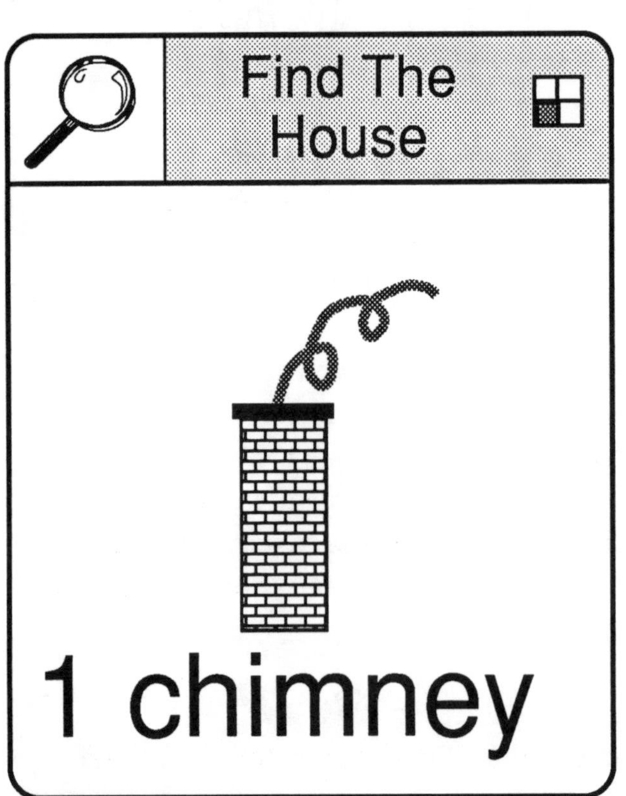

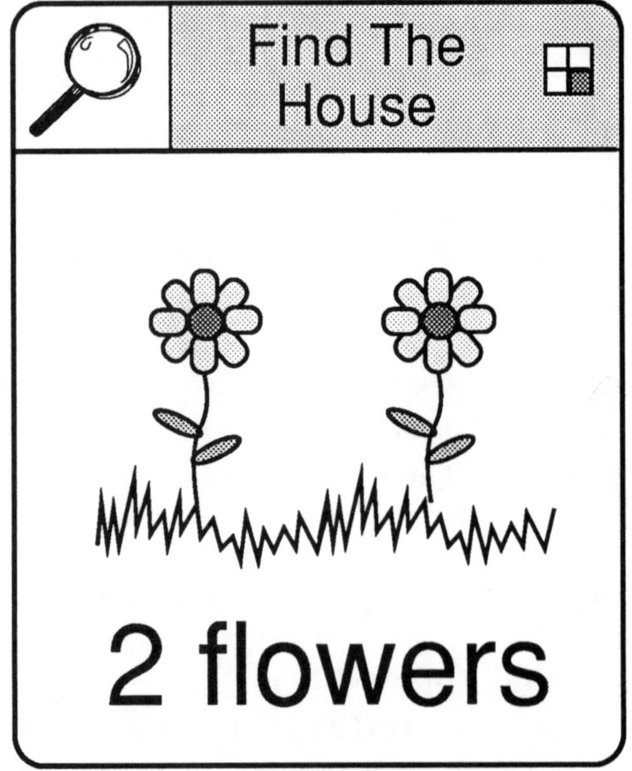

TEACHER NOTES: Duplicate this page on a different color paper than the "Find The House" picture cards. Tell the students that they will need to find the house that fits all four clues.

"Find The House" Picture Cards

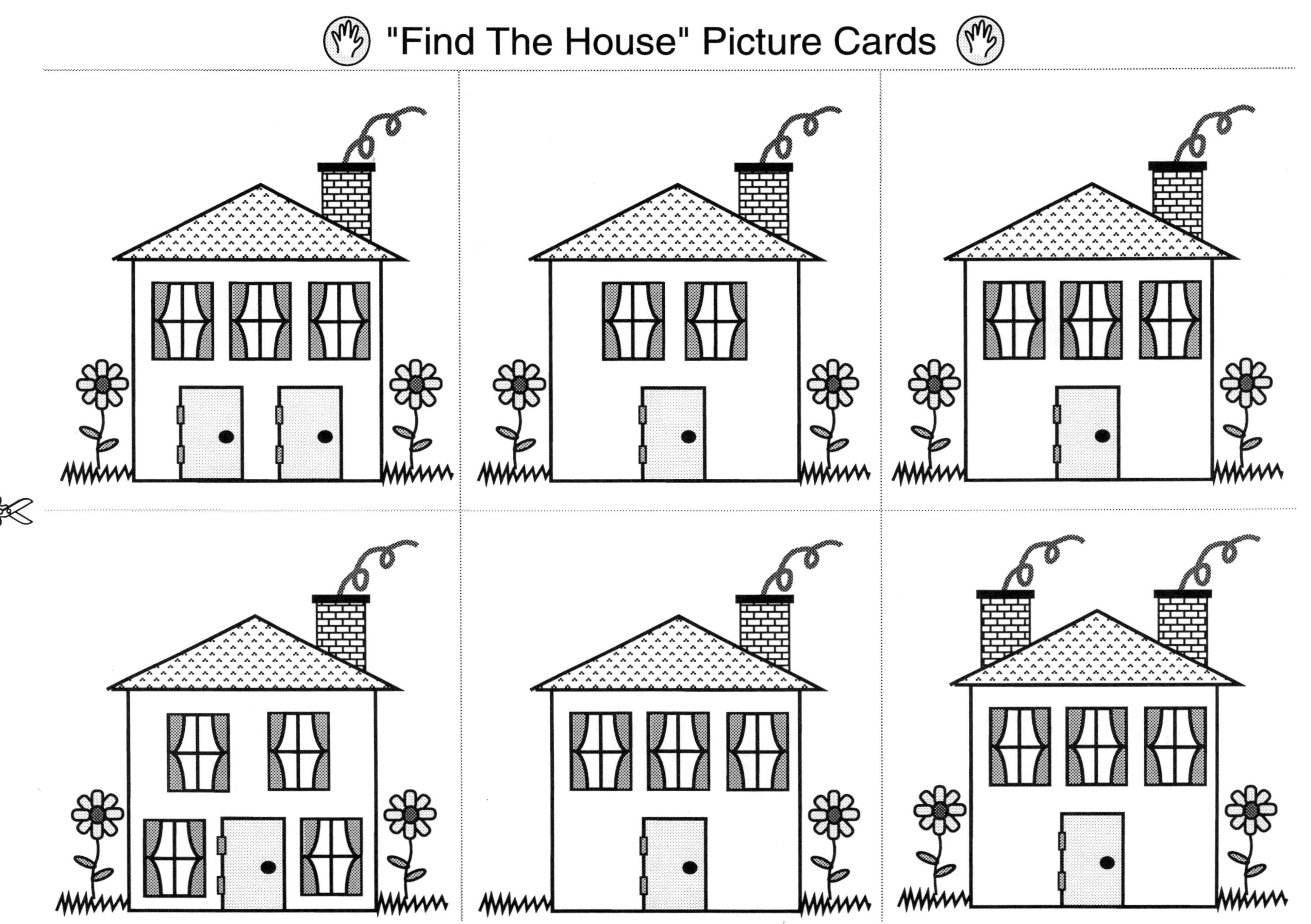

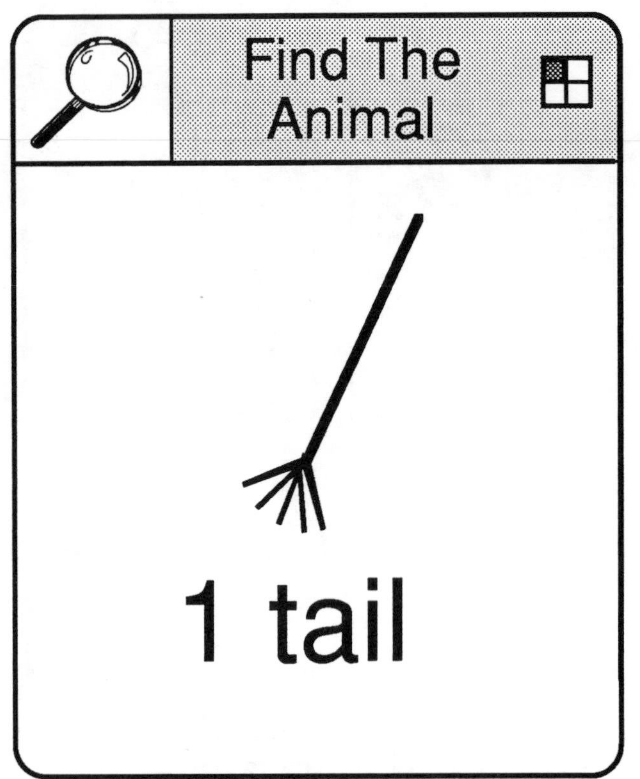

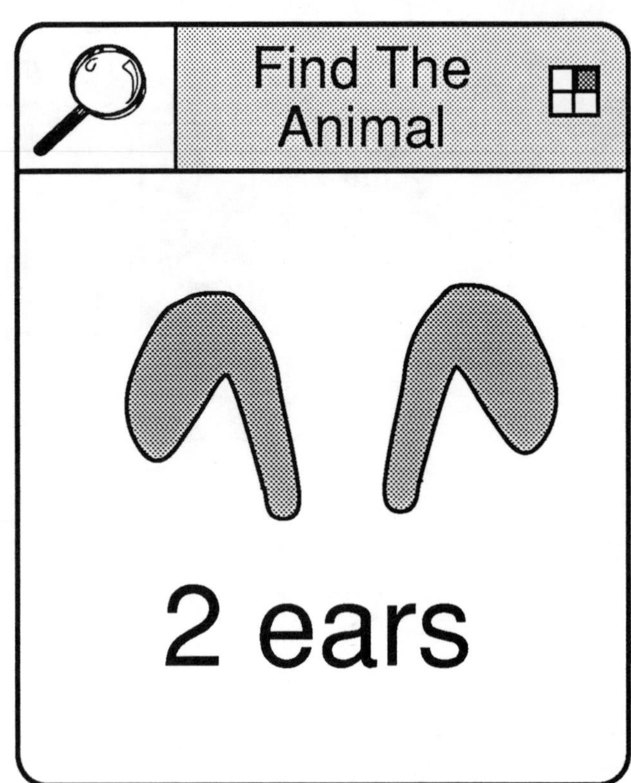

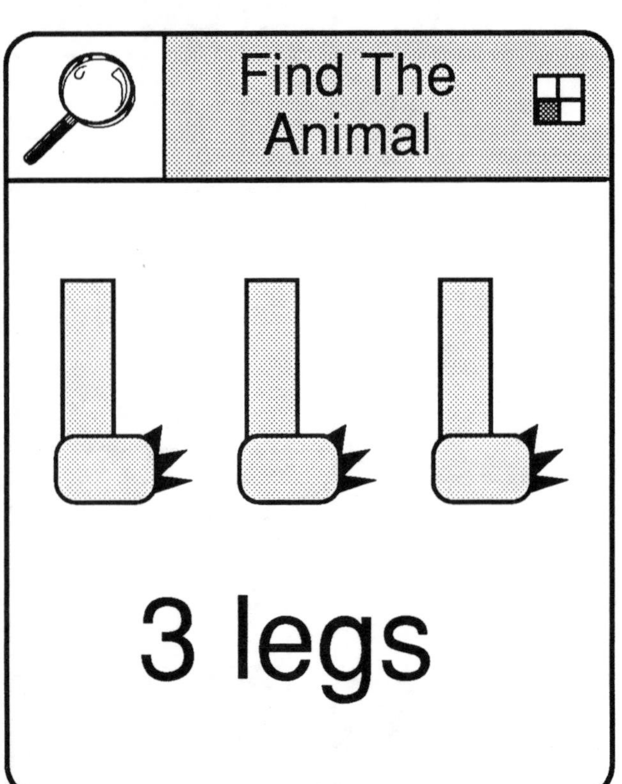

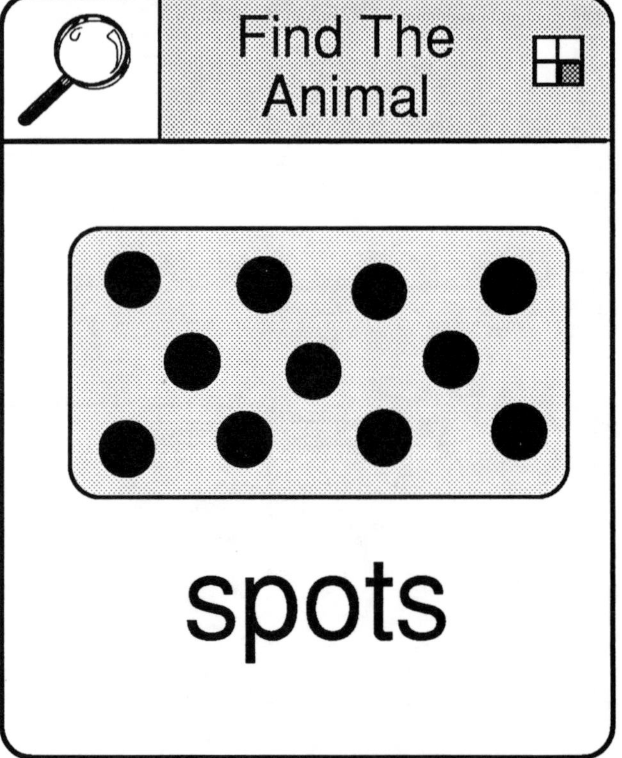

TEACHER NOTES: Duplicate this page on a different color paper than the "Find The Animal" picture cards. Tell the students that they will need to find the animal that fits all four clues.

"Find The Animal" Picture Cards

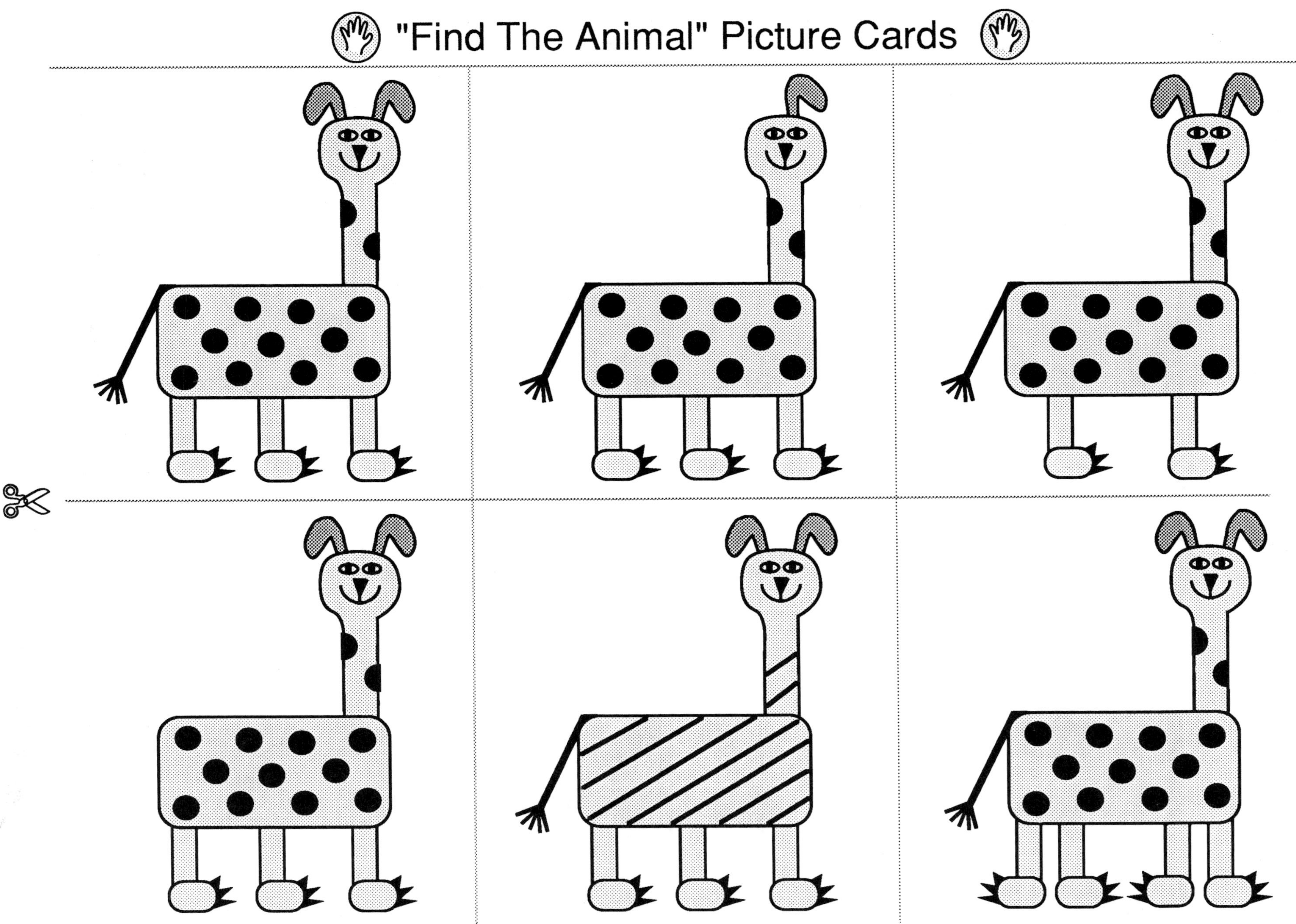

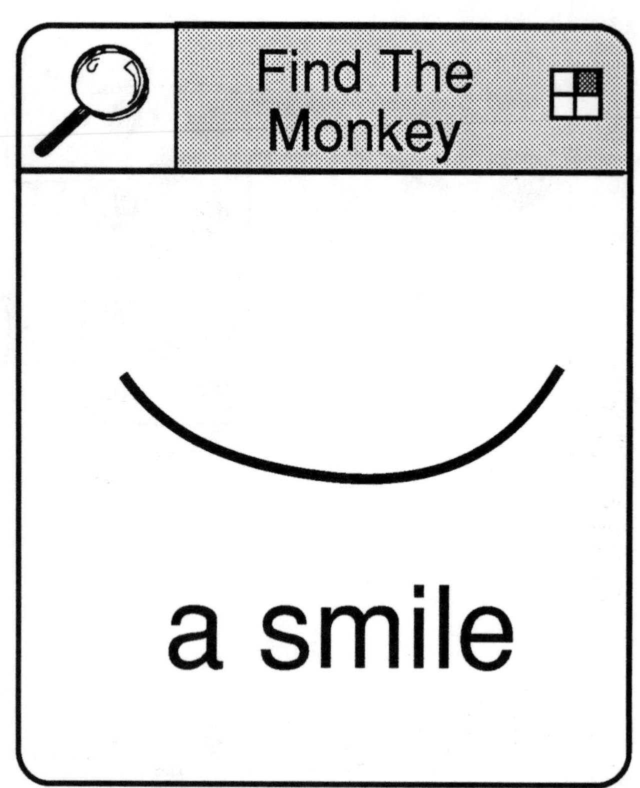

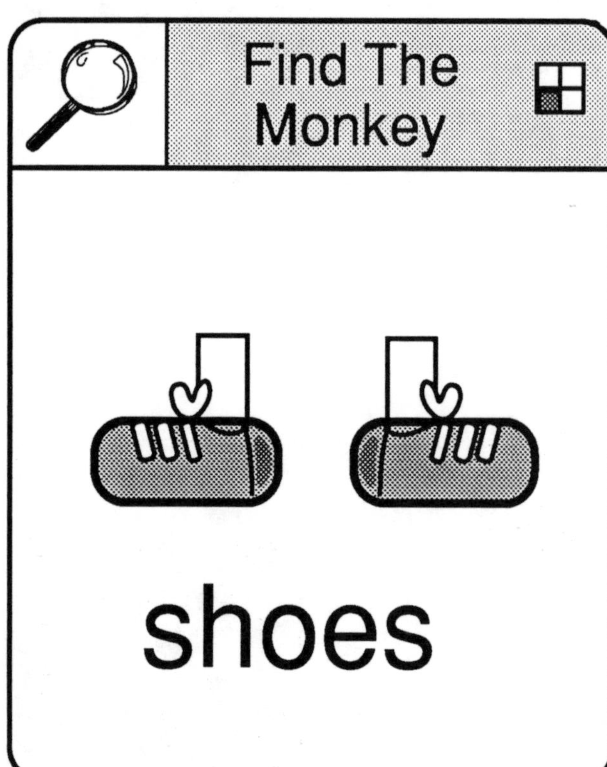

TEACHER NOTES: Duplicate this page on a different color paper than the "Find The Monkey" picture cards. Tell the students that they will need to find the monkey that fits all four clues.

"Find The Monkey" Picture Cards

Find The
Pet Shop
The pet shop has
2 rabbits.

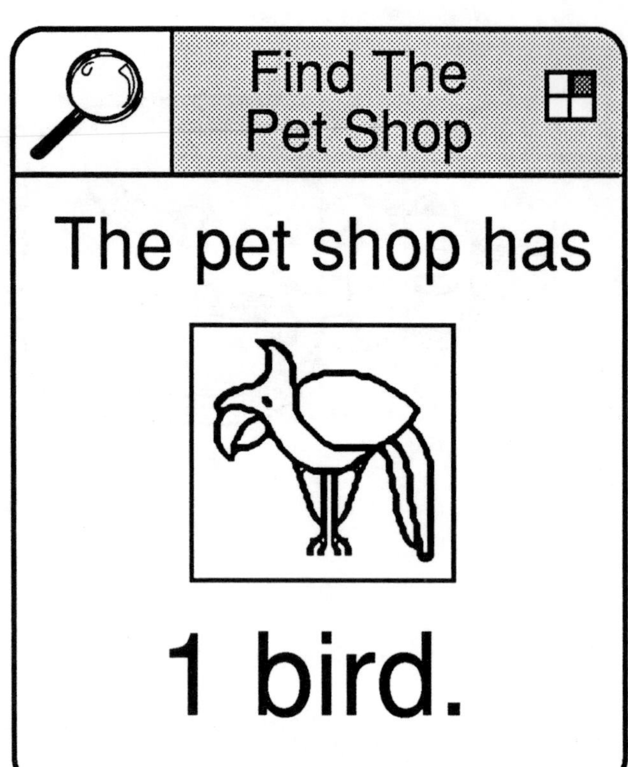

Find The
Pet Shop
The pet shop has
1 bird.

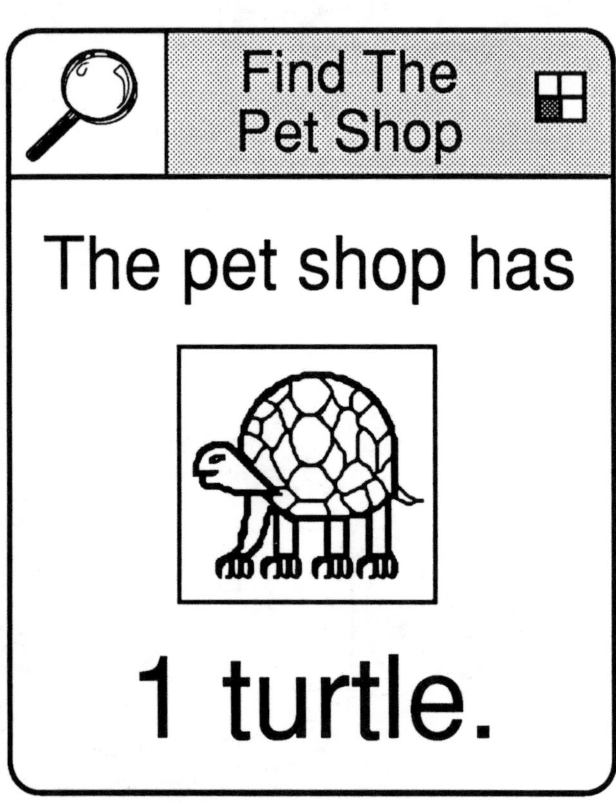

Find The
Pet Shop
The pet shop has
1 turtle.

Find The
Pet Shop
The pet shop has
1 fish.

TEACHER NOTES: Duplicate this page on a different color paper than the "Find The Pet Shop" picture cards. Tell the students that they will need to find the pet shop that fits all four clues.

"Find The Pet Shop" Picture Cards

PETS

PETS

PETS

PETS

PETS

PETS

Find The Bear
The bear has a happy face.

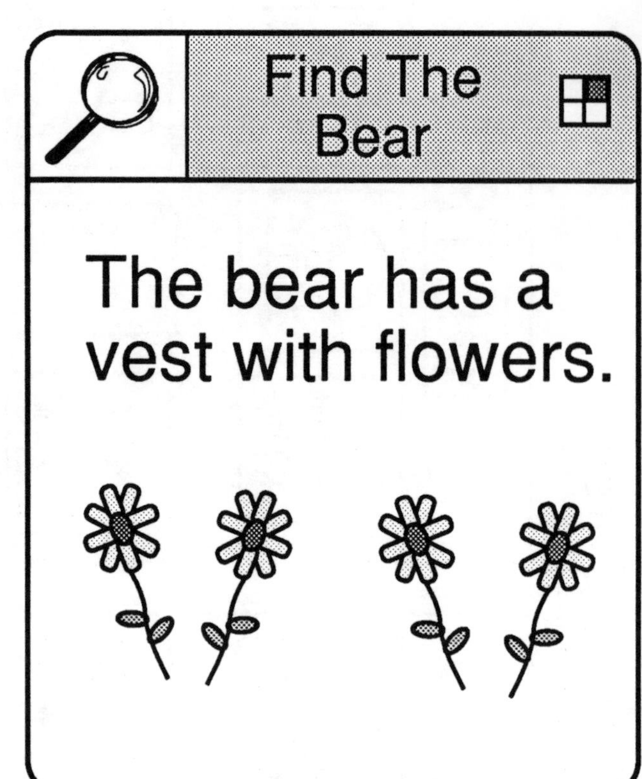

Find The Bear
The bear has a vest with flowers.

Find The Bear
The bear has a vest with 4 buttons.

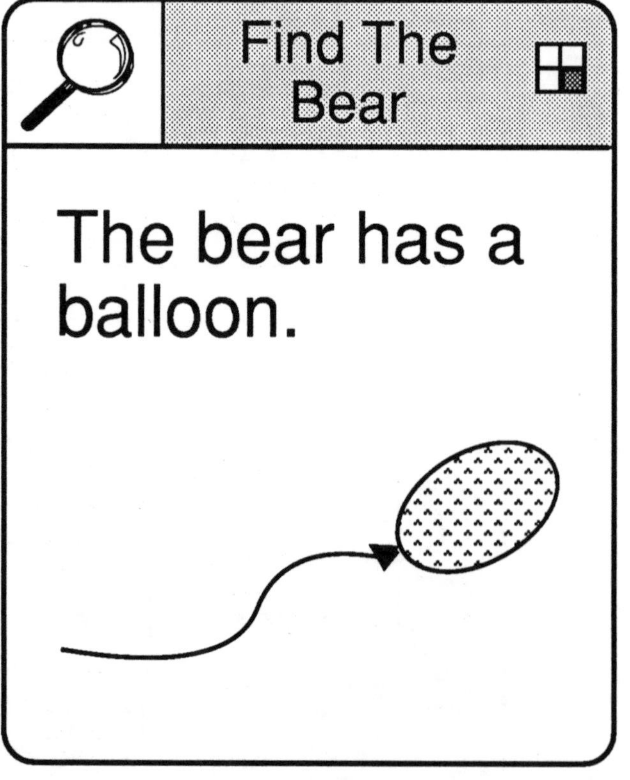

TEACHER NOTES: Duplicate this page on a different color paper than the "Find The Bear" manipulatives. Tell the students that they will need to find the bear that fits all four clues.

"Find The Bear" Picture Cards

Find Rosa's Robot

Rosa's robot has a triangle for a body.

Find Rosa's robot!

Find Rosa's Robot

Rosa's robot has more than 2 arms.

Find Rosa's robot!

Find Rosa's Robot

Rosa's robot has an even number of square buttons.

Find Rosa's robot!

Find Rosa's Robot

Rosa's robot has more wheels than arms.

Find Rosa's robot!

 TEACHER NOTES: Duplicate this page on a different color paper than the "Find Rosa's Robot" picture cards. Tell the students that they will need to find the robot that fits all four clues.

"Find Rosa's Robot" Picture Cards

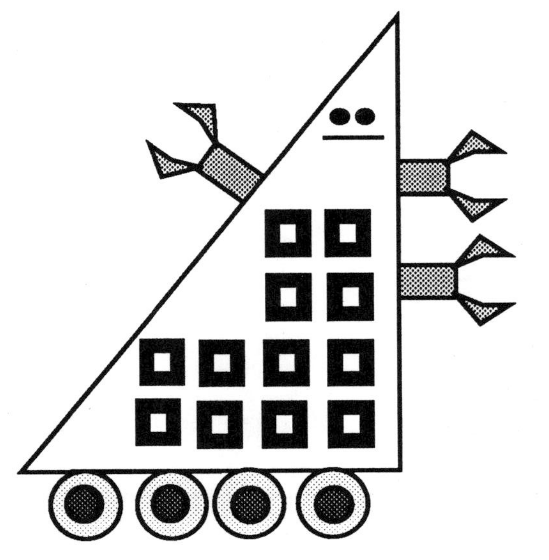

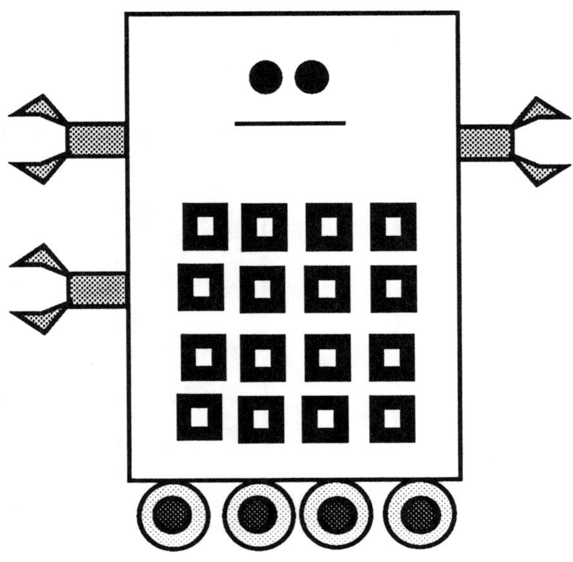

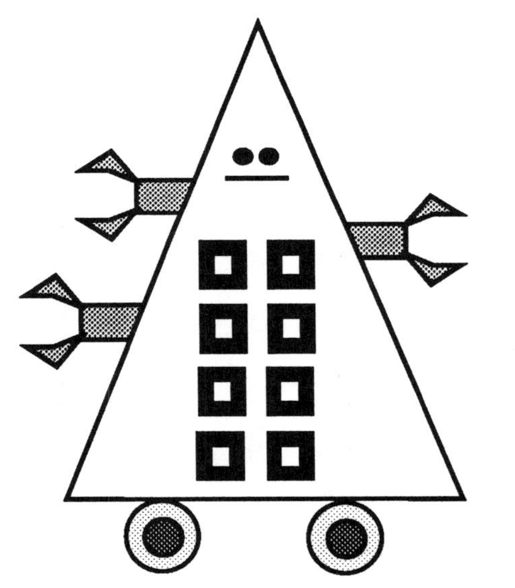

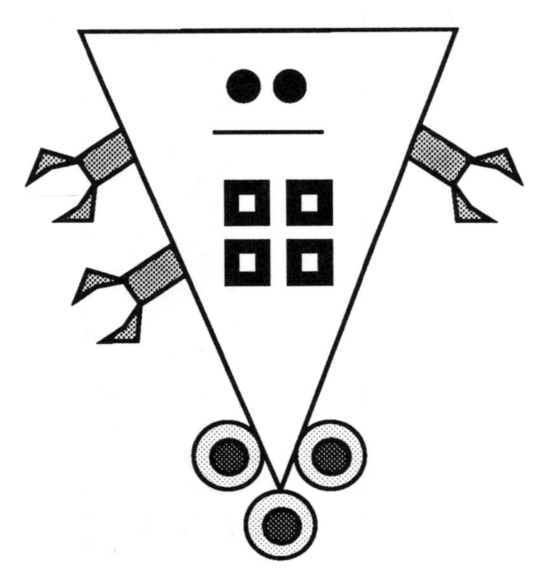

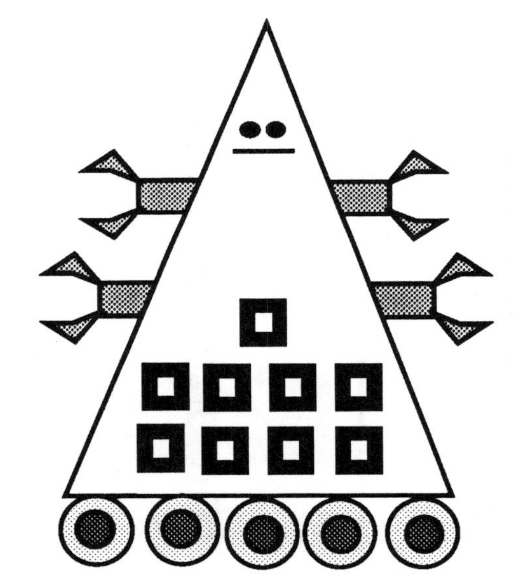

Find The Pizza - 1

The pizza is round.

Find the pizza.

Find The Pizza - 1

The pizza's topping is mushrooms.

Find the pizza.

Find The Pizza - 1

The pizza is cut into six slices.

Find the pizza.

Find The Pizza - 1

Two slices of the pizza have no topping.

Find the pizza.

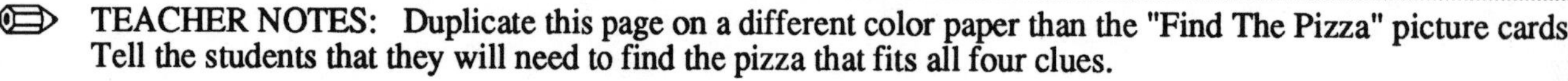

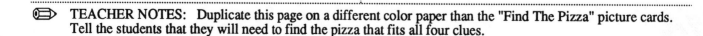

TEACHER NOTES: Duplicate this page on a different color paper than the "Find The Pizza" picture cards. Tell the students that they will need to find the pizza that fits all four clues.

"Find The Pizza - 1" Picture Cards

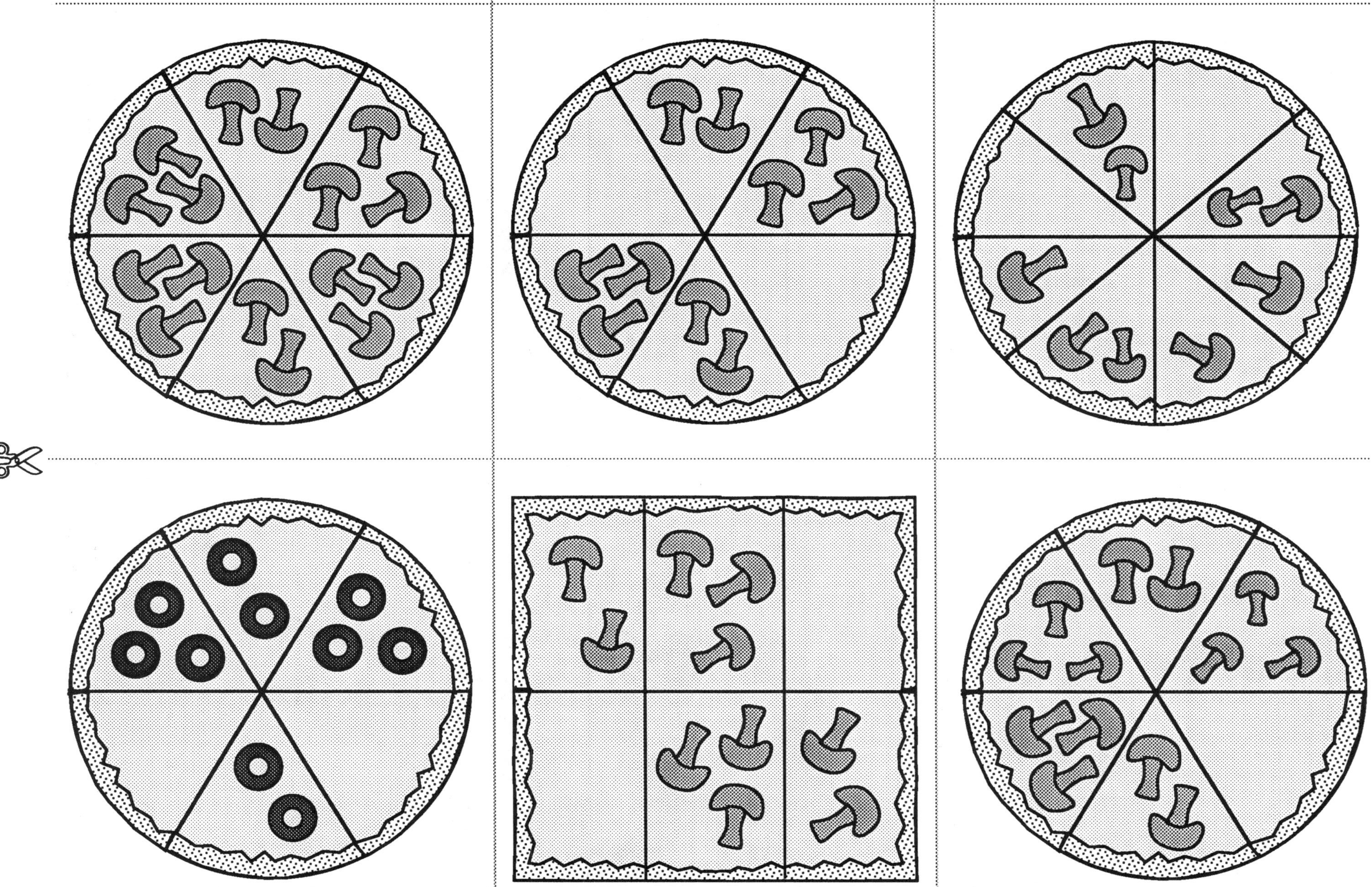

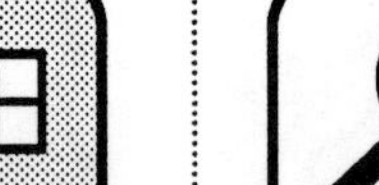

The pizza is cut into eighths.

Find the pizza.

Find The Pizza - 2

Half of the slices have toppings.

Find the pizza.

The pizza has three more mushrooms than olives.

Find the pizza.

Find The Pizza - 2

The pizza has an odd number of olives.

Find the pizza.

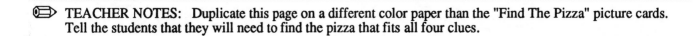

TEACHER NOTES: Duplicate this page on a different color paper than the "Find The Pizza" picture cards. Tell the students that they will need to find the pizza that fits all four clues.

"Find The Pizza - 2" Picture Cards

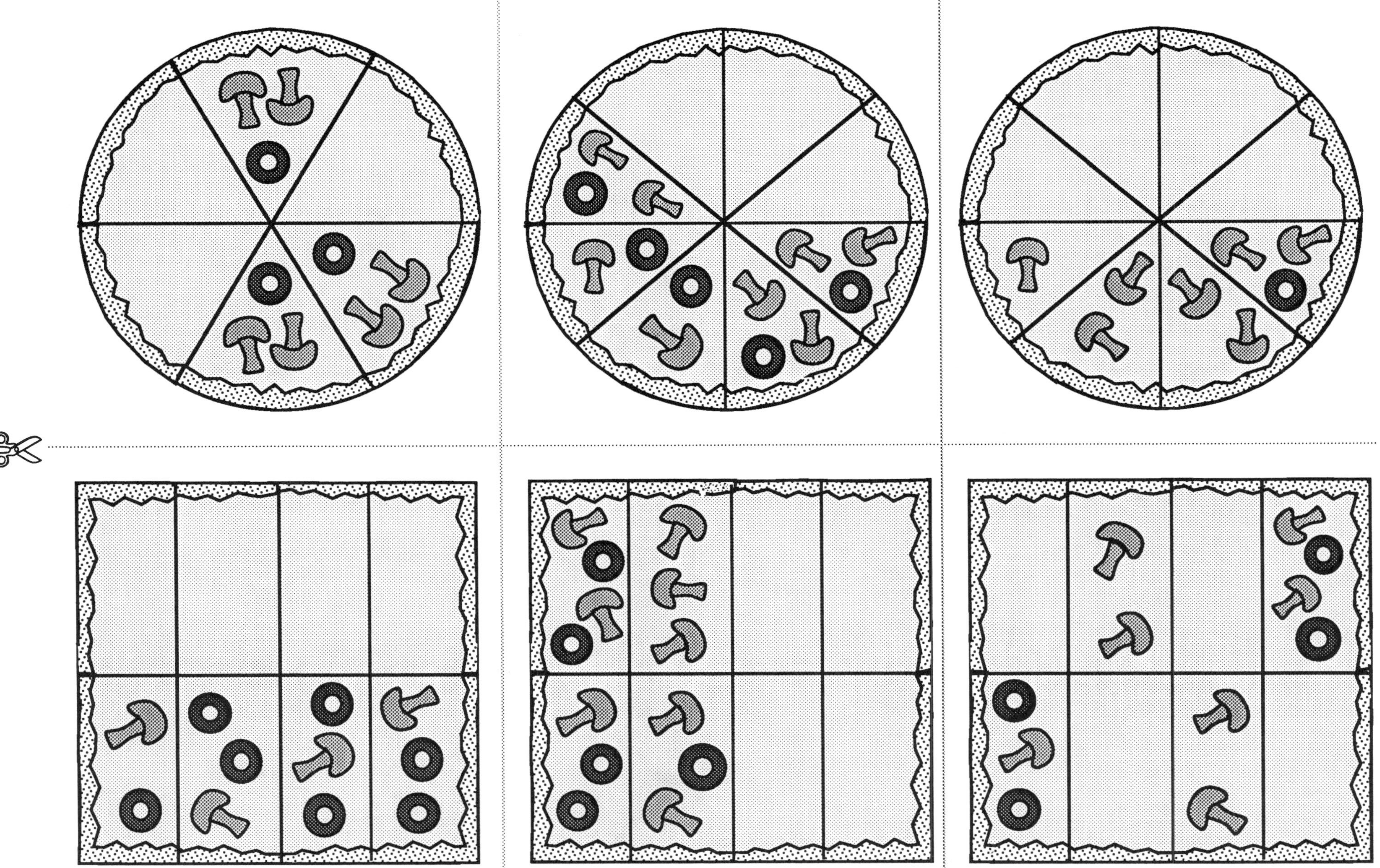

Pizza Match - 1

Pedro's pizza has an equal number of mushrooms and olives.

Find Pedro's pizza.

Pizza Match - 1

On Irma's pizza, one-third of the slices have toppings.

Find Irma's pizza.

Pizza Match - 1

Zeke's pizza is cut into sixths.

Find Zeke's pizza.

Pizza Match - 1

Anna hates olives.

Find Anna's pizza.

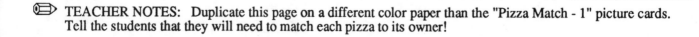

 TEACHER NOTES: Duplicate this page on a different color paper than the "Pizza Match - 1" picture cards. Tell the students that they will need to match each pizza to its owner!

"Pizza Match -1" Picture Cards

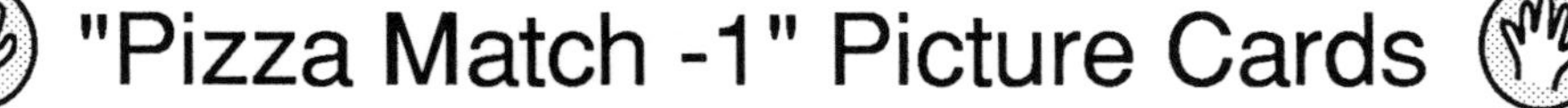

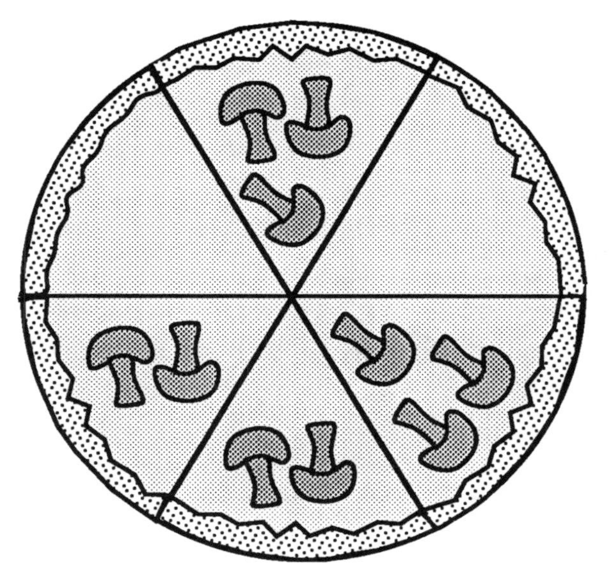

Pedro

Irma

Zeke

Anna

Pizza
Match - 2

Arturo's pizza has olives on half of its slices.

Find Arturo's pizza.

Pizza
Match - 2

Zina's pizza was cut into fourths, but she cut each slice in half because the pieces were too big.

Find Zina's pizza.

Pizza
Match - 2

Iris' pizza has twice as many mushrooms as Zina's pizza.

Find Iris' pizza.

Pizza
Match - 2

The four kids can equally share the mushrooms on Pat's pizza, but they can not share the olives equally.

Find Pat's pizza.

TEACHER NOTES: Duplicate this page on a different color paper than the "Pizza Match - 2" picture cards. Tell the students that they will need to match each pizza to its owner!

"Pizza Match - 2" Picture Cards

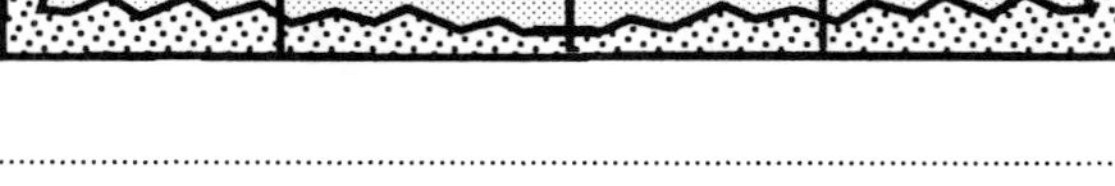

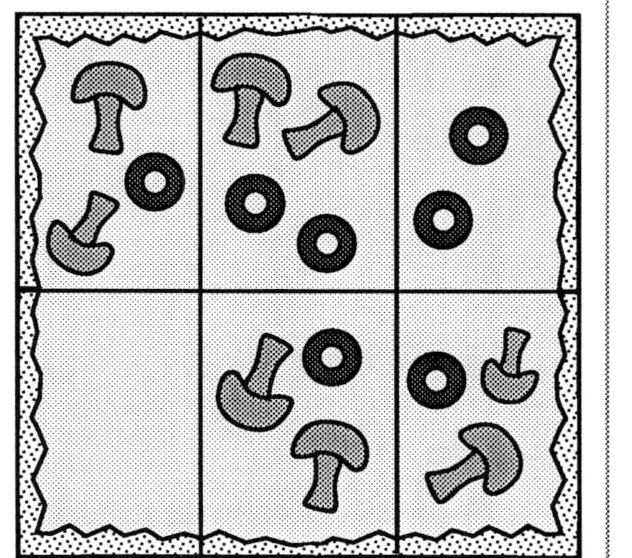

Pat

Iris

Zina

Arturo

Bear Line-up # 4
A red bear is in the front of the line. Two yellow bears are at the back of the line.

Bear Line-Ups

OVERVIEW

With **BEAR LINE-UPS**, students work together to arrange small plastic or paper bears in a variety of ways. Before they begin, the children need time to freely explore the red, yellow, blue and green bears. Then, students share clues that tell them how to put the bears in order. As each clue is read, the bears are re-arranged to incorporate the new information. Younger children organize the bears in a single line on mats provided in each envelope. When all the bears are arranged, the groups check that their line-up matches all the clue cards. As the activities progress in difficulty, students move on to put bears in two lines, and finally, in groups. If you leave the bears in an area that is accessible to students, your class will often choose to make their own Bear Line-Ups during free time!

Skills

- ➤ Sorting
- ➤ Sequencing
- ➤ Counting
- ➤ Directionality
- ➤ Spatial visualization
- ➤ Deductive reasoning
- ➤ Communication

Concepts and Vocabulary

- ➤ **Colors:** red, blue, yellow, green
- ➤ **Directions:** front, back, middle, in front of, in back of, behind, between
- ➤ **Ordinal numbers:** first, second, third, fourth, fifth, sixth …

	Suggested Grade Levels					
Activity	K	1	2	3	4	5
Bear Line-Up 1–4	✓	✓	✓			
Bear Line-Up 5		✓	✓			
Bear Line-Up 6 and 7			✓	✓		
Bear Line-Up 8 and 9			✓	✓	✓	
Bear Line-Up 10 and 11				✓	✓	✓

GETTING READY

Each cooperative group will need a collection of at least five bears in each of these colors: red, green, blue and yellow. We suggest that you use **teddy bear counters** because they are extremely appealing to children and can be used for many activities in the classroom (for example, dramatic play, counting, patterning, word problems). Sources to purchase teddy bear counters are listed on page 138.

You may also use the **Bear Line-Up Manipulatives** on page 75 at the end of this section. Duplicate the Bear Line-Up Manipulatives on red, green, blue and yellow copy paper. Then, cut out the bears and give each group a collection of at least 4–5 bears in each color.

If you color in the featured bear or bears on each **clue card** for **Bear Line-Ups 1–4**, the clues will be easier for children to read.

Mats for Bear Line-Ups 1–6 are provided at the end of this section. These mats help each group to form one line-up in their work spaces. The mats are especially important for students in Grades K-1 and should be included in each envelope.

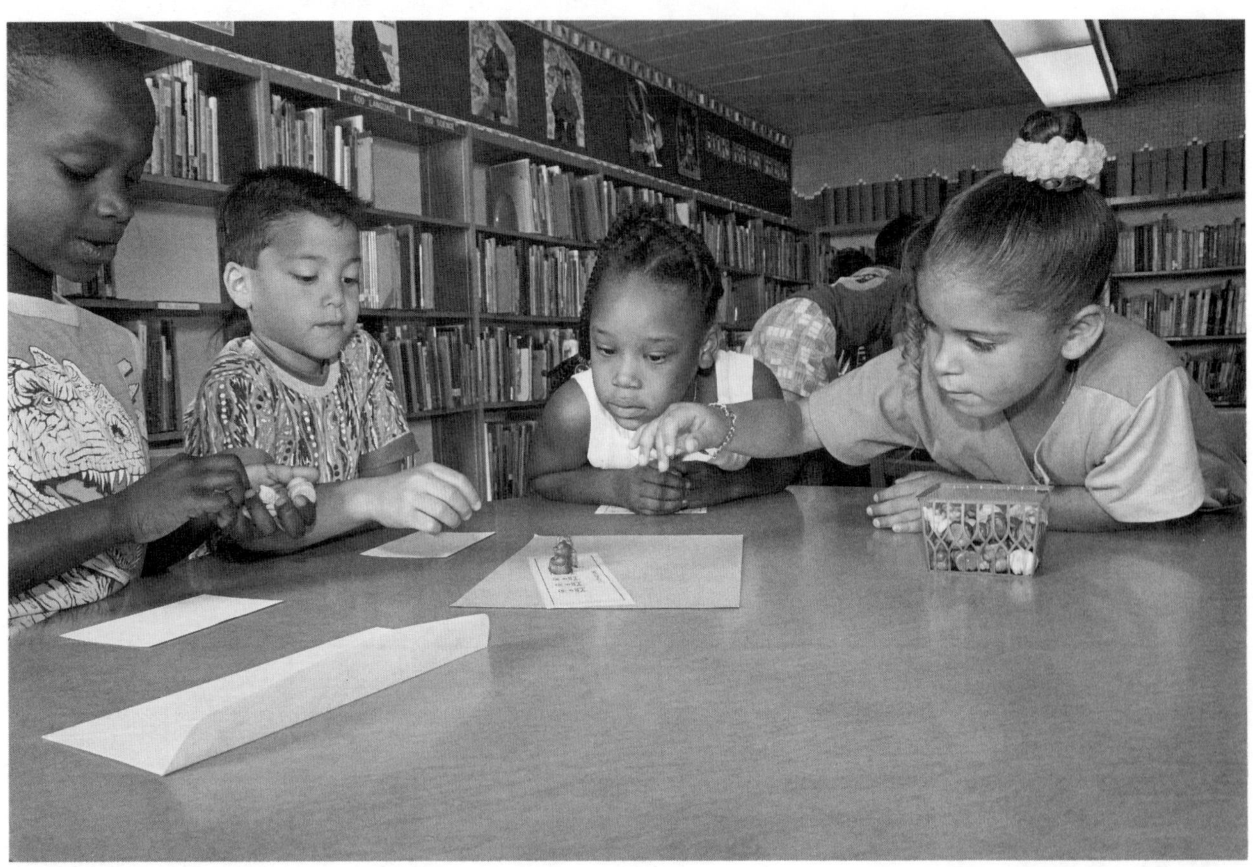

OPTION: You may wish to enlarge the faces of the bears and duplicate them on colored paper to create a set of bears that can be used (as masks or necklaces) to model the cooperative logic process (see Tips For Teachers on page 60).

INTRODUCTORY ACTIVITIES

Student Line-Up

To introduce essential reading and listening vocabulary, choose several students. Have the students form a straight line, one at a time, according to your directions. Begin with simple directions, for example, "Juanita, you will be at the front of the line. Paul, go to the back of the line. Jessie, stand just in back of Juanita." The instructions can also be more complex, for example, "Pedro, stand between Pat and Malcolm. Janet, you are just behind a girl and just in front of a boy." Incorporate ordinal numbers, for example, "Jesus is first in line. Kamala is third in line. Leann is last in line. Chad is second in line." Then, have student volunteers use oral directions to line up their classmates.

Lunch/Recess Line-Up

You may wish to allow extra time to line up students for lunch or recess with oral directions! Choose one student to stand at the front of the line. Ask this student to direct one classmate to stand in the line. After each student lines up, she then will direct a classmate to stand in line. Continue until all students are lined up. Have each student make a statement about their position in the line, for example, "I am first. I am behind two girls. I am in front of Irma."

Free Exploration

Distribute the plastic bears to the students. Allow ample time for them to explore the collections before you proceed with Bear Line-Ups. Ask each group to tell you what they have discovered about their collections, for example, the total number of bears, the number of bears in each color, the features of the bears, whether or not the distribution of bears is equal. This will give students a chance to play with the bears before they are asked to use them to solve a specific cooperative logic problem.

NOTE: Students are likely to engage in dramatic play with the bears. It may be helpful to add a building material (for example, cubes, blocks) to enhance this activity.

Bear With Me

Ask students to hypothesize why a group of bears might need to line up. Perhaps they're at a bank, the grocery store or in a relay race. Incorporate the students' ideas as you introduce the cooperative logic problems, for example, "These four bears want to climb a very small tree. They can't decide who should be first and they've asked you to help. In this envelope are four clues that will help you decide!"

TIPS FOR TEACHERS

Logistics

The bear counters are a very attractive manipulative! In order to prevent loss of bears, ask students take an inventory of their bear collection before and after the activity period. The inventory is a good opportunity to practice "hands-on" addition, multiplication and graphing skills. You may also need to discuss ways to share the bears equitably.

Grades K–2

It is important to demonstrate a sample bear line-up with your students. You can do this with large felt bears or enlarged copies of bear faces in four colors. Students can also become the bears with hats, pieces of construction paper or bear faces (see "Getting Ready") in red, yellow, blue and green. Proceed as described below in an example from **Bear Line-Up 1**.

Choose four students to represent the bears that are needed for the line-up (one red, one blue, one yellow, one green). Choose four other students and give each child one clue card. Ask each student to read a clue card (for example, "The green bear is last"). Then direct the appropriate bear/child to line up in the correct place. Encourage students to describe the position of the bear in the line, rather than show the group the clue. Proceed with the clues, one at a time, until all of the bears are in line. Review each clue card to validate that the line-up is accurate.

> *OPTION: At first, you may wish to provide enough bears and mats for each student in the group to solve the problem. Have each student read her clue. After each clue is read, group members will arrange the bears according to the information that is revealed.*

Young children need ample time to play with the bears and figure out how to divide them up for the activity. Many groups decide to give each group member a particular color bear. They make a rule that you are only allowed to move the bears that are yours. This system encourages all children to listen to all the clues because the information will tell them how to line up their particular bears.

Bear Line-Ups 1-4 feature pictures of four to six bears in one line. Though the clues may seem simple, challenge your students to cover up their clue and then describe the position of the bear on their card. This will promote vocabulary development and active listening.

Grades 3–4

Bear Line-Ups 8, 9 and **11** have multiple solutions. Encourage students to solve the problems in more than one way. **Bear Line-Ups 10** and **11** require students to use six clues to put the bears in groups. All previous Bear Line-Ups use four clues to put the bears in one or two lines. You may wish to discuss this change before proceeding with **Bear Line-Up 10**. Students will need to make an agreement about how to distribute the clues equitably.

ASSESSMENT

Grades K–2

Students can color in their solutions to **Bear Line-Ups 1–6** on white copies of the **Bear Line-Up Mats**. You can also duplicate the **Bear Line-Up Manipulatives** (page 75) on four colors of paper (red, yellow, green, blue). Pre-cut the bears individually or in strips. Have each student paste down bears to record the group's solution on a sheet of paper. Older students can add a sentence to describe their picture.

Grades 2–4

Ask each student to draw their solution and write about the process used by their group to line up the bears. Students should explain why they are sure their solution is correct.

GOING FURTHER

Free Exploration Revisited

We have found that free exploration is dramatically different when students have an opportunity to play with the bears after they have completed several Bear Line-Ups. For example, in several first grade classrooms, students spontaneously created a series of very structured Bear Line-Ups with complex patterns and sequences of bears!

Design a Line-Up

Have students create their own Bear Line-Ups and draw or paste them on paper. Young students can dictate words to describe the order or use invented spelling to write their own description of the line-up.

Guess My Pattern

In this game, students arrange their Line-Ups in patterns (for example, red, blue, blue, red, blue, blue). Classmates then try to continue the patterns by adding bears to the line. The patterns may be simple or complex, based on the students' ability levels.

Bear Coach

For this activity, students work as partners. Place a folder or other barrier between the two students. Have one student (the coach) line up a specified number of bears (for example, three to five bears in Grades K-1, eight to ten bears in Grades 2-4) behind the barrier. The coach must then describe to the partner how to line up the bears. The goal is for both partners to create the same line of bears. This can be checked when the barrier is lifted. Older students can write a set of clues to tell their partner how to arrange the bears.

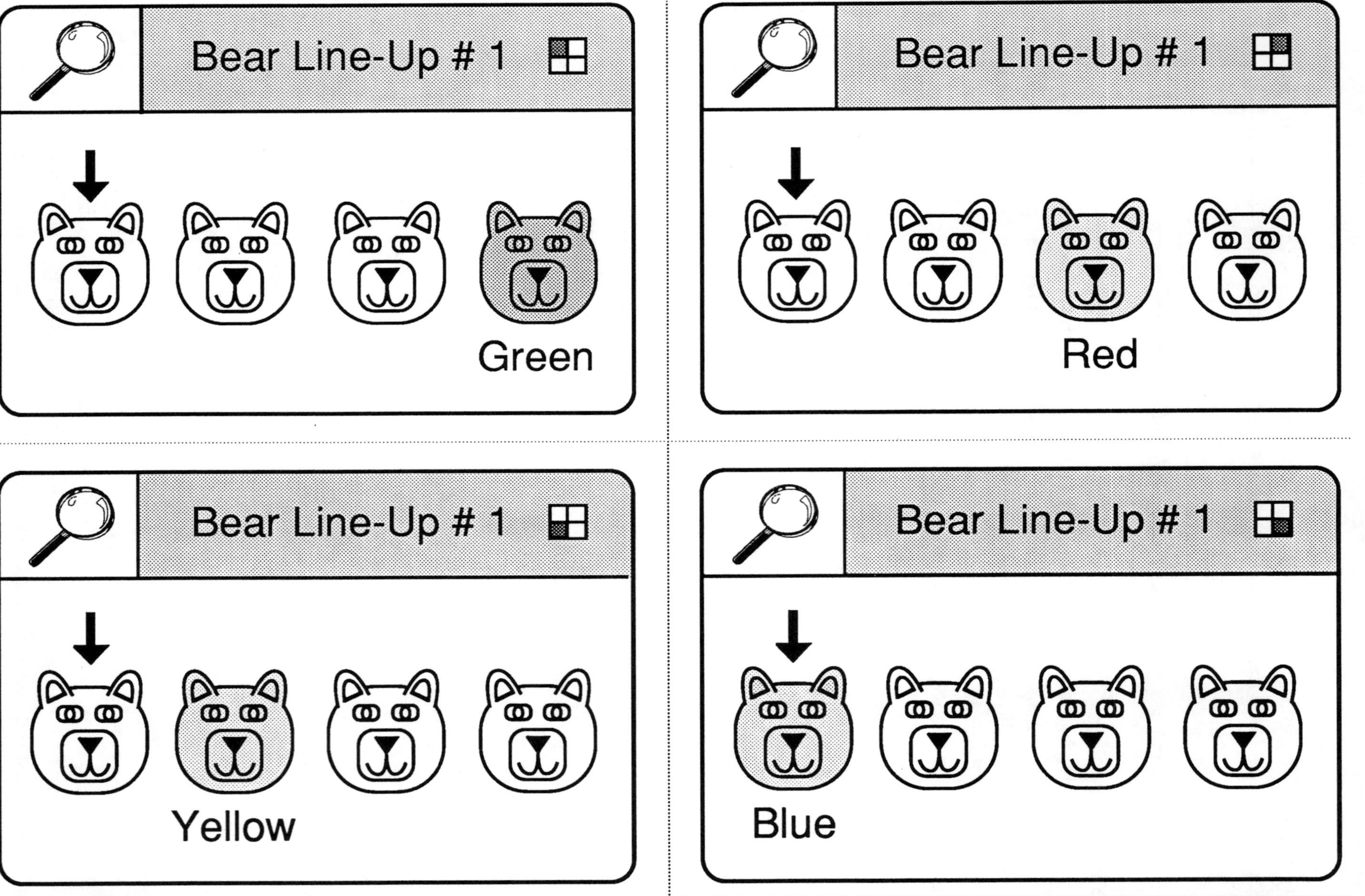

TEACHER NOTES: If you color in the featured bear/s on each card, it will be easier for children to read. The arrow indicates the first bear in line. Each group will need five bears in each of the following colors: red, green, blue and yellow. Students should line up the bears according to clue cards.

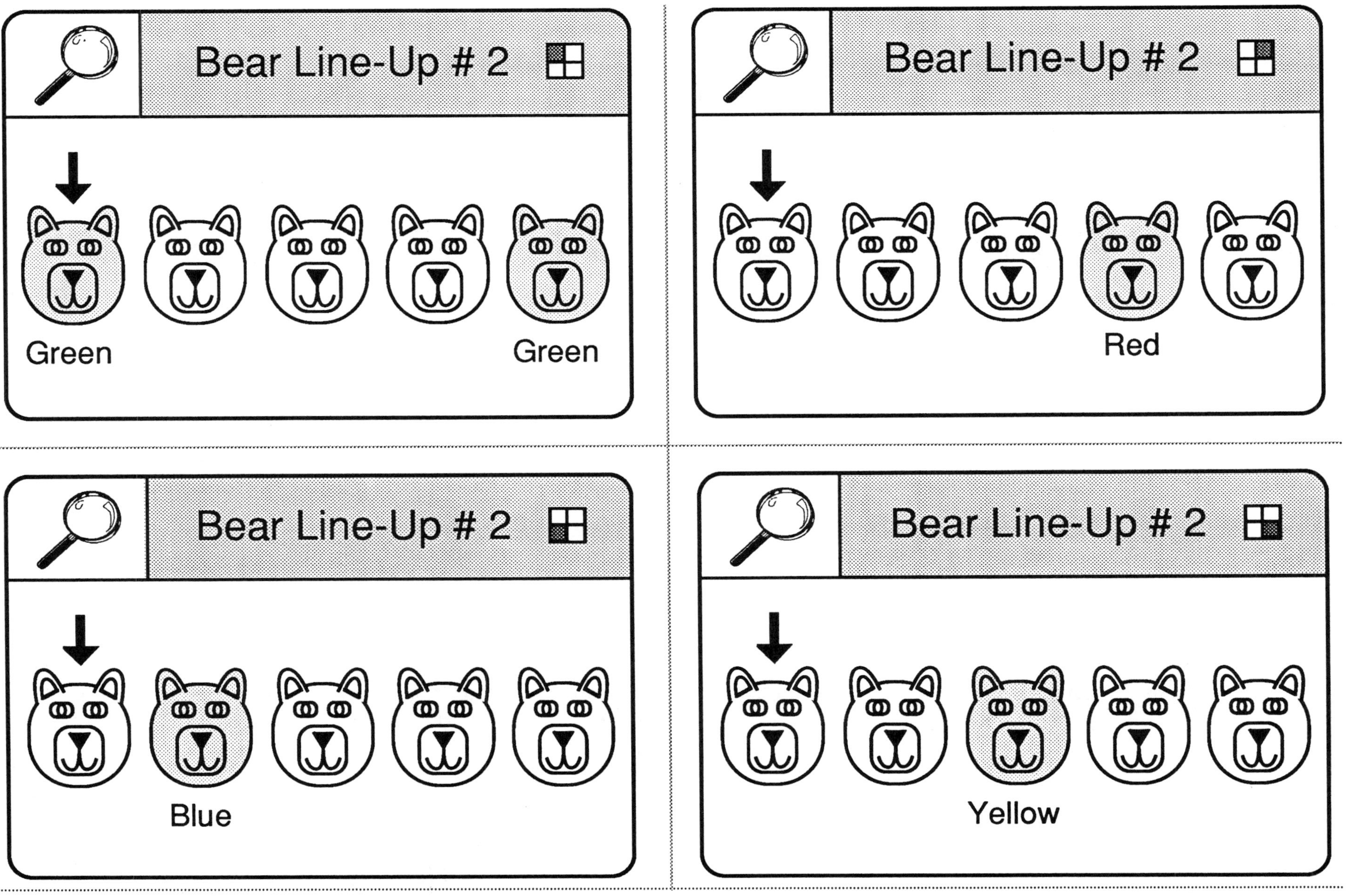

TEACHER NOTES: If you color in the featured bear/s on each card, it will be easier for children to read. The arrow indicates the first bear in line. Each group will need five bears in each of the following colors: red, green, blue and yellow. Students should line up the bears according to clue cards.

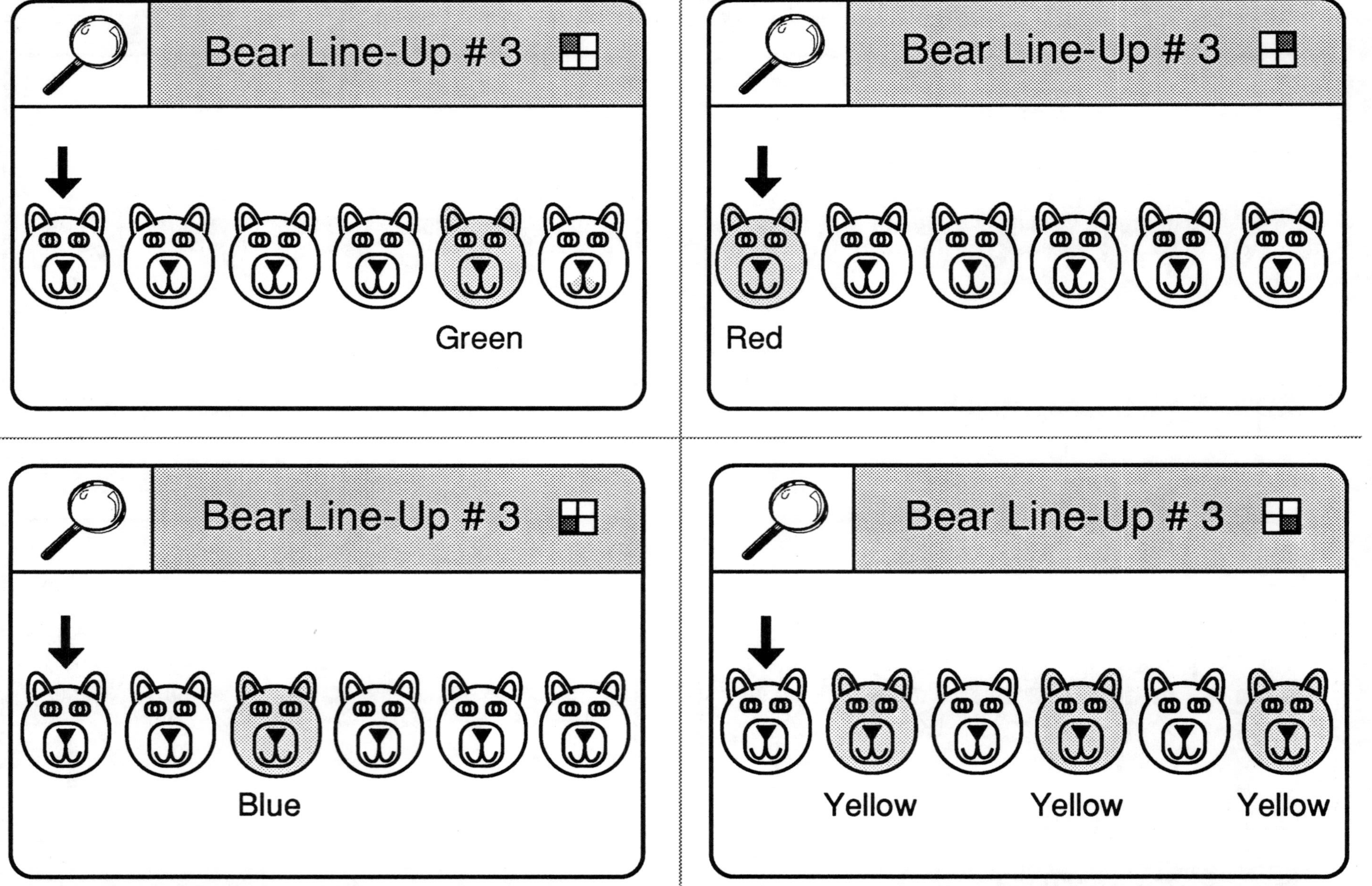

TEACHER NOTES: If you color in the featured bear/s on each card, it will be easier for children to read. The arrow indicates the first bear in line. Each group will need five bears in each of the following colors: red, green, blue and yellow. Students should line up the bears according to clue cards.

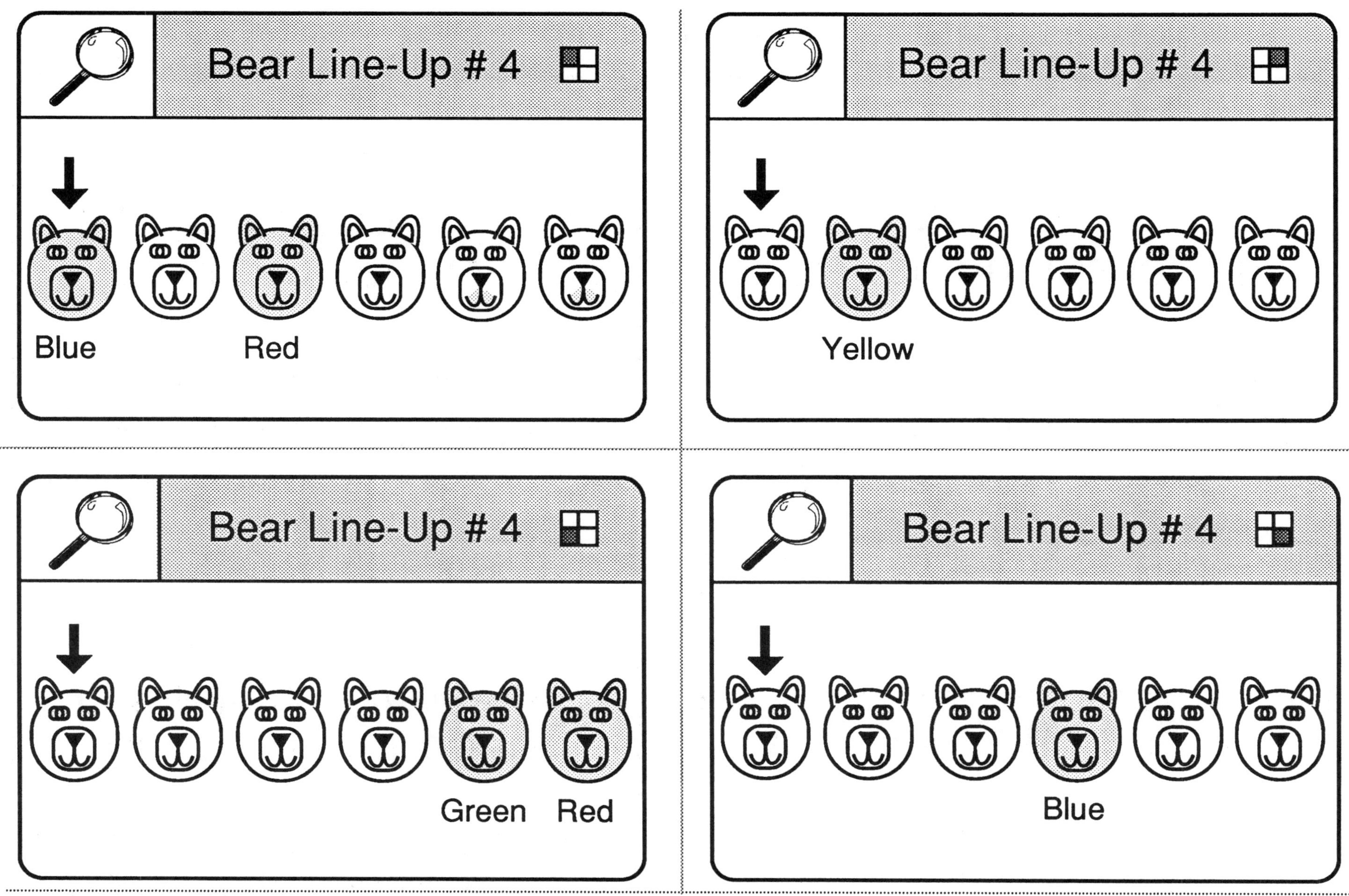

TEACHER NOTES: If you color in the featured bear/s on each card, it will be easier for children to read. The arrow indicates the first bear in line. Each group will need five bears in each of the following colors: red, green, blue and yellow. Students should line up the bears according to clue cards.

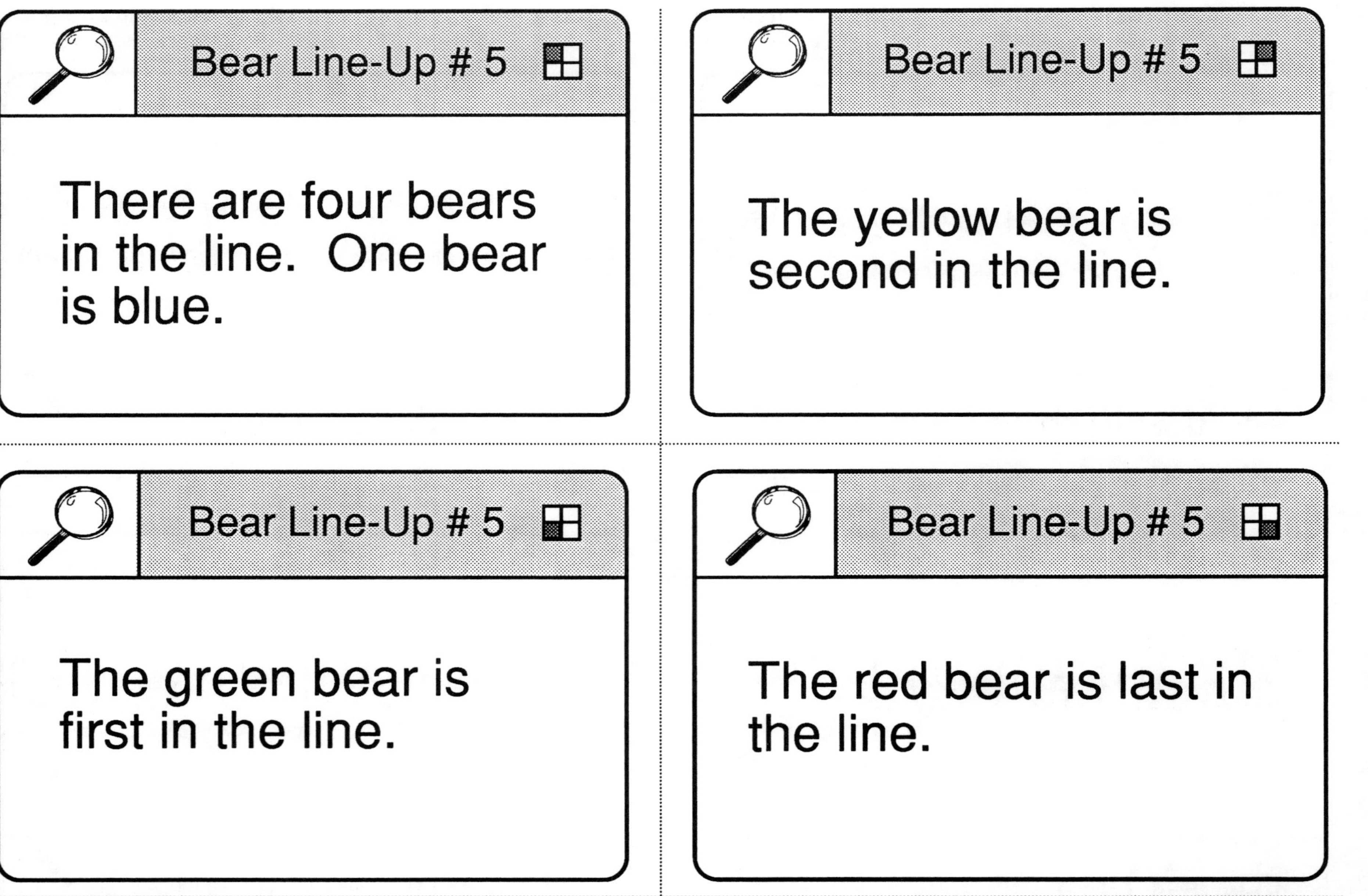

Bear Line-Up # 5
There are four bears in the line. One bear is blue.
Bear Line-Up # 5
The yellow bear is second in the line.
Bear Line-Up # 5
The green bear is first in the line.
Bear Line-Up # 5
The red bear is last in the line.

TEACHER NOTES: Each cooperative group will need five bears in each of these colors: red, green, blue and yellow. Students should line up the bears according to clue cards.

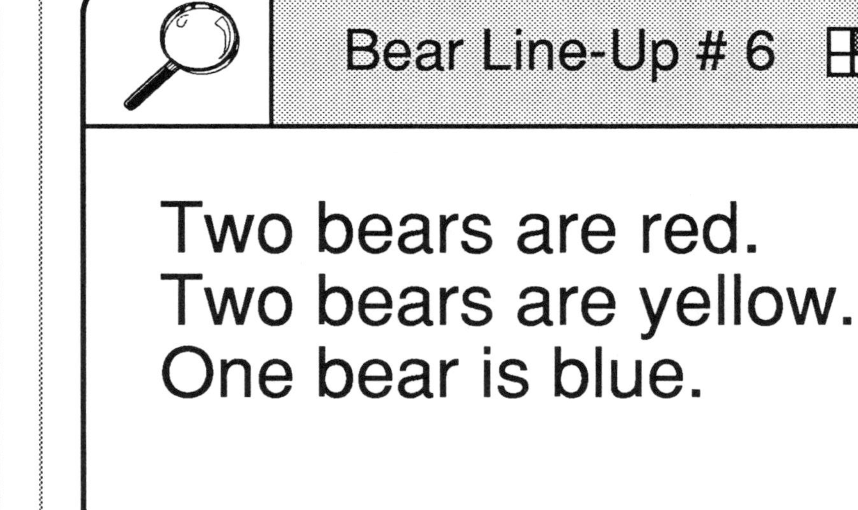

Bear Line-Up # 6

There are five bears in line.

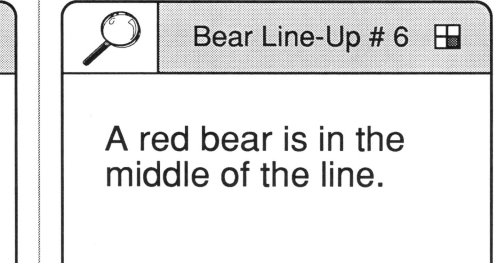

Bear Line-Up # 6

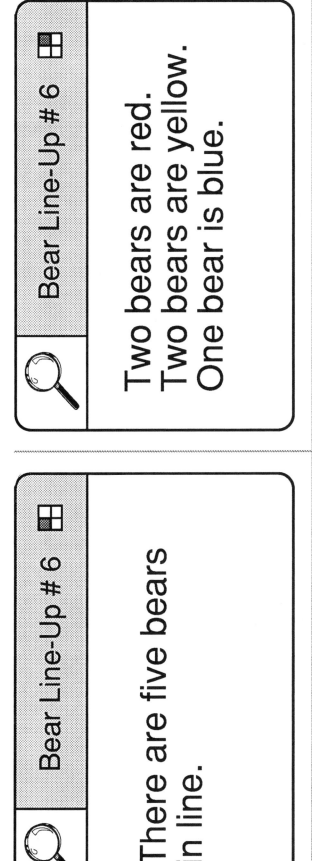

Two bears are red.
Two bears are yellow.
One bear is blue.

Bear Line-Up # 6

A red bear is in the front of the line. Two yellow bears are at the back of the line.

Bear Line-Up # 6

A red bear is in the middle of the line.

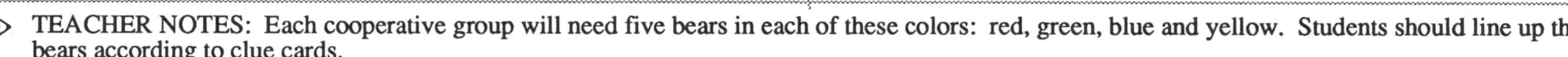

TEACHER NOTES: Each cooperative group will need five bears in each of these colors: red, green, blue and yellow. Students should line up the bears according to clue cards.

Bear Line-Up # 7

There are 2 red bears, 2 yellow bears, 2 green bears and 2 blue bears in the line.

Bear Line-Up # 7

One yellow bear is first in the line. One yellow bear is last in the line.

Bear Line-Up # 7

Two red bears are just in front of 2 green bears in the line.

Bear Line-Up # 7

Two blue bears are just behind 2 green bears in the line.

TEACHER NOTES: Each cooperative group will need five bears in each of these colors: red, green, blue and yellow. Students should line up the bears according to clue cards.

Bear Line-Up # 8

There are 2 lines of bears. There are 5 bears in each line.

Bear Line-Up # 8

One green bear is at the front of each line.

Bear Line-Up # 8

In one line, a red bear is between 2 blue bears. In the other line, a blue bear is between 2 red bears.

Bear Line-Up # 8

A yellow bear is at the back of one line. A green bear is at the back of the other line.

TEACHER NOTES: Each cooperative group will need five bears in each of these colors: red, green, blue and yellow. Students should line up the bears according to clue cards. THIS PROBLEM HAS MORE THAN ONE SOLUTION!

Bear Line-Up # 9

There are 2 lines of bears. There are 7 bears in each line.

Bear Line-Up # 9

Three green bears are at the front of one line.

Bear Line-Up # 9

In one line, there are 3 blue bears and 4 yellow bears. Each blue bear is just behind a yellow bear.

Bear Line-Up # 9

Four red bears are at the back of one line.

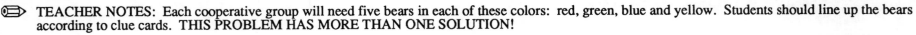

TEACHER NOTES: Each cooperative group will need five bears in each of these colors: red, green, blue and yellow. Students should line up the bears according to clue cards. THIS PROBLEM HAS MORE THAN ONE SOLUTION!

Bear Line-Up # 10

There are 4 groups of bears. There are 4 bears in each group.

Put the bears in groups!

Bear Line-Up # 10 

There are 4 red bears, 4 green bears, 4 yellow bears and 4 blue bears.

Put the bears in groups!

Bear Line-Up # 10

One group has 2 green bears. One group has 2 red bears.

Put the bears in groups!

Bear Line-Up # 10 

Each group has exactly one yellow bear.

Put the bears in groups!

Bear Line-Up # 10

One group has only blue and yellow bears.

Put the bears in groups!

Bear Line-Up # 10 

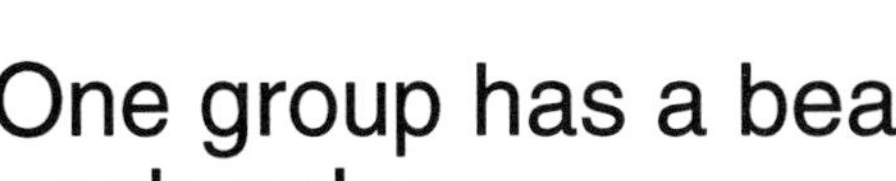

One group has a bear of each color.

Put the bears in groups!

 TEACHER NOTES: Each cooperative group will need at least five bears in each of these colors: red, green, blue and yellow. Students should put the bears in groups, according to their clue cards. REMIND THE STUDENTS THAT THIS PROBLEM HAS SIX CLUE CARDS TO BE SHARED IN THE GROUP.

Bear Line-Up # 11

There are 5 groups of bears. Each group has 3 bears.

Put the bears in groups!

Bear Line-Up # 11

There are 5 red bears, 4 green bears, 3 yellow bears and 3 blue bears.

Put the bears in groups!

Bear Line-Up # 11

In one group, all the bears are red.

Put the bears in groups!

Bear Line-Up # 11

Two groups look the same.

Put the bears in groups!

Bear Line-Up # 11

Blue bears are found in 3 groups.

Put the bears in groups!

Bear Line-Up # 11

Every group with a blue bear also has a yellow bear.

Put the bears in groups!

TEACHER NOTES: Each cooperative group will need at least five bears in each of these colors: red, green, blue and yellow. Students should put the bears in groups, according to their clue cards. THIS PROBLEM HAS SIX CLUE CARDS AND HAS MORE THAN ONE SOLUTION!

"Bear Line-Up" Mats
(for Line-Ups 1–3)

TEACHER NOTES: Include a copy of the appropriate mat in each envelope for Bear Line-Ups 1–3. The mat should be duplicated on a different color paper than the Bear Line-Up clues. The mats help groups orient themselves at their table or desk. The arrow indicates the beginning of the line. If you make additional copies of the mats on white paper, students can use them to record group or individual solutions.

"Bear Line-Up" Mats
(for Line-Ups 4–6)

TEACHER NOTES: Include a copy of the appropriate mat in each envelope for Bear Line-Ups 4–6. The mat should be duplicated on a different color paper than the Bear Line-Up clues. The mats help groups orient themselves at their table or desk. The arrow indicates the beginning of the line. If you make additional copies of the mats on white paper, students can use them to record group or individual solutions.

"Bear Line-Up" Manipulatives

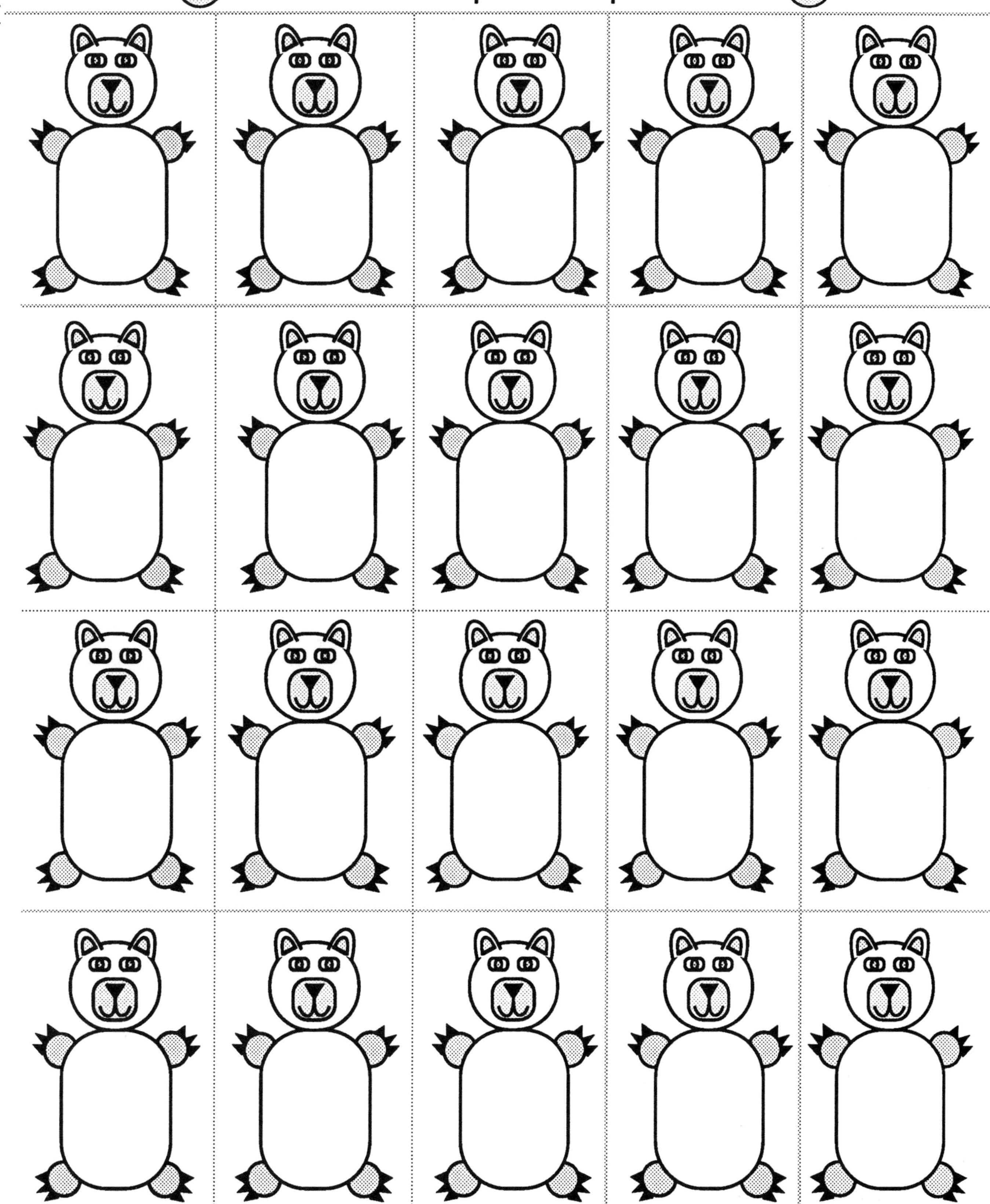

TEACHER NOTES: You will need four colors of bears: red, blue, yellow and green. To save time, this page can be duplicated on the four colors of copy paper. Or, you can duplicate them on white paper and color them with markers or crayons. Cut out the bears and put them in sets of at least 20 bears equally divided in four colors.

? ? ? ?

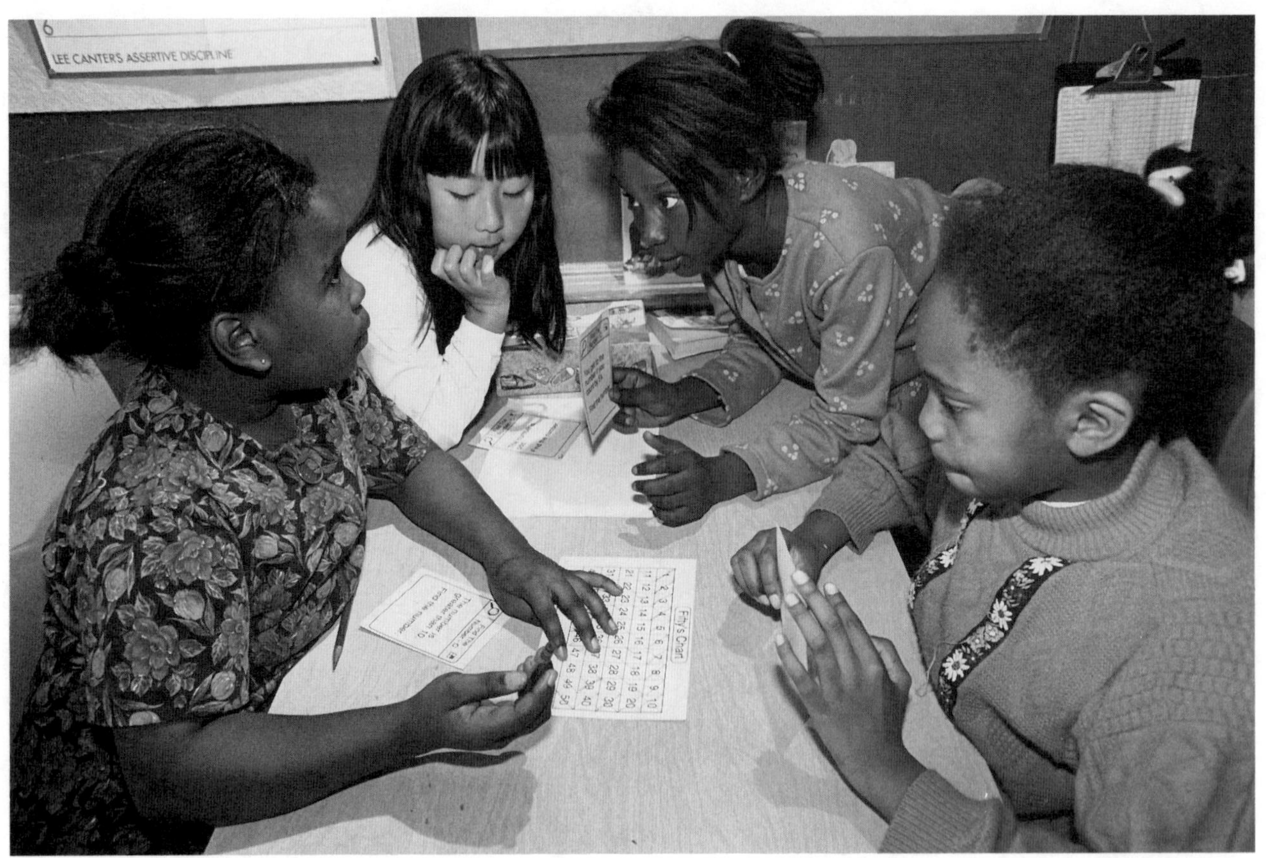
LEE CANTER'S ASSERTIVE DISCIPLINE

? ? ? ?

? Secret Number ?

OVERVIEW

In the **SECRET NUMBER** family of cooperative logic problems, students in **Grades 2–4** become "number detectives." They try to find a particular number that has all the properties listed on their clue cards. As each clue is read, the detectives record the information on the Fifty or Hundred charts. They cross out numbers that are eliminated by the clues until only one number remains. Then, the group checks again to confirm that the secret number has all of the characteristics listed on the clues. The Fifty and Hundred charts provide visual evidence that the case has been solved.

Skills

- Counting by 2's, 5's, 7's, 10's, and 20's
- Greater than, less than
- Use of Fifty and Hundred charts
- Place Value
- Deductive reasoning
- Communication

Concepts and Vocabulary

- **Numeration and Computation:** greater than, less than, larger than, more than, odd, even, digit, ones' place, tens' place, add, sum, half, count by … (skip counting)

Suggested Grade Levels						
Activity	**K**	**1**	**2**	**3**	**4**	**5**
Secret Number A–C			✓	✓	✓	
Secret Number D				✓	✓	
Secret Number E–H				✓	✓	✓

Logic activities in this section are designed for **Grades 2-4**. However, teachers in **Grade 1** can use the introductory activities to help students become familiar with the Hundred Chart and number patterns. **Kindergarten** students can use a number line from one to ten or twenty to explore the concepts of larger and small numbers; and the order of numbers (for example, nine comes before ten; seven is between six and eight).

NOTE: The Hundred Chart is an essential tool for numeration, computation, place value, mental math and patterning for students in Grades 2-4. Although students at this level should be able to use the Hundred Chart, we use the Fifty Chart in ***Secret Number A-C*** *to simplify the process of elimination. These three first problems also utilize beginning number patterns and concepts (for example, counting by 5's; odd/even).*

GETTING READY

Each cooperative group will need the Fifty Chart (**Secret Number A–C**) or Hundred Chart (**Secret Number D–H**). The charts are at the end of this section. Students will need a marker or pencil to eliminate numbers as clues are revealed. You may wish to laminate a class set of Hundred Charts and have students use grease pencils or "dri-mark" pens to cross out the numbers. These charts can then be re-used after they are erased.

OPTION: You may wish to make an overhead transparency of the Hundred Chart to demonstrate how to eliminate numbers that don't fit the information from the clues.

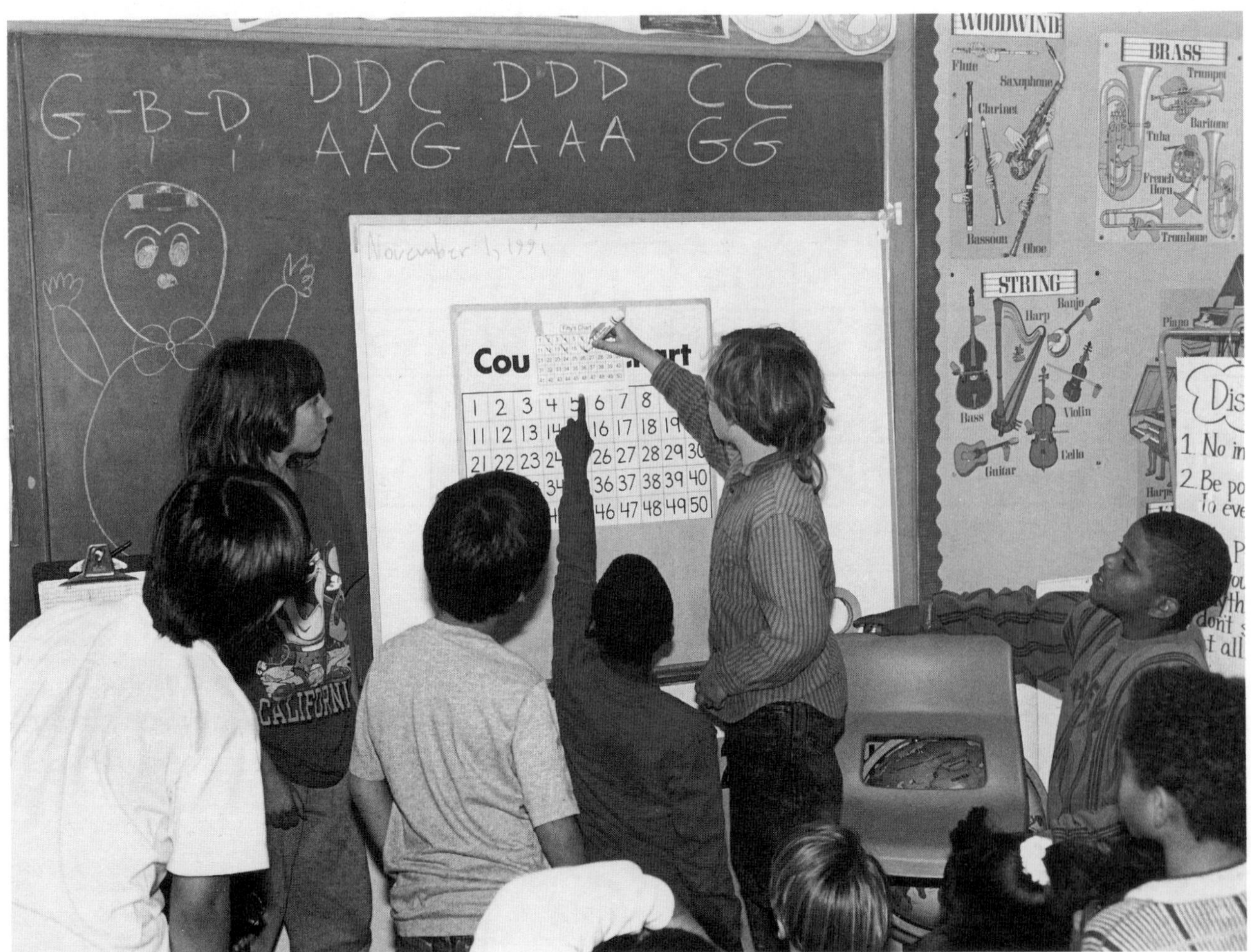

A **large laminated Wall Chart** is an additional teaching tool to help students see number patterns and learn how to eliminate numbers on their individual Hundred Chart. (See page 138 for sources of where to purchase the wall and laminated student charts.)

INTRODUCTORY ACTIVITIES

Exploration of the Hundred Chart

Distribute a Hundred Chart to each student. Have students work with partners to look closely at the chart and list their discoveries. For example: "There are numbers all over the chart. The highest number is 100. The lowest number is 1. There are 10 rows of numbers. There are ten numbers in each row. Every number that is under the `5' has a five in the ones' place." Create a list of the students' discoveries.

Chart Patterns

Distribute a Hundred Chart to each student. Have students work in partners to color in patterns on the Hundred Chart. If a large Hundred Chart is available, have students show their patterns to the class. Appropriate patterns include:

Grade 2: Counting by 2's, 5's, 10's
Grade 3: Counting by 2's, 3's, 4's, 5's, 10's, 20's
Grade 4: Counting by 2's, 3's, 4's, 5's, 6's, 7's, 8's, 9's, 10's, 20's.

If students have difficulty counting, they can cover numbers on the chart with beans or counting chips. For example, if a student is counting by 3's, she will cover the first two numbers and color in the third. You can also count and clap number patterns. For example, for the number 3, students would count "1, 2" and clap as they say "3." Then they'd continue to count "4, 5" and clap as they say "6."

Guess My Number

Use this game to reinforce key vocabulary and concepts from Secret Number activities. Write the numbers from one through ten on the chalkboard or display them on a large Hundred Chart. Explain to the students that you are thinking of a number between one and ten. Tell them that they can guess your number by asking "yes" or "no" questions, for example: "Is it even? Is it less than five? Do you get to it when you count by 5's?" As each question is asked, cross out numbers that are eliminated by the answer to the question. Tally the number of questions it takes for the students to guess the number.

When students become proficient at the game, increase the range of numbers to 20, 50 and 100. Have students use Fifty or Hundred charts to eliminate numbers. You may also ask volunteers to choose numbers and conduct the game with their classmates.

TIPS FOR TEACHERS

Recording the Clues

The Secret Number family requires students to use the Hundred Chart to record information from their clues. This process can be difficult for some students. It is essential that you model the use of the Hundred Chart before you proceed with Secret Number activities. "Guess My Number" (see "Introductory Activities") is a perfect game to help students learn to eliminate numbers and record possibilities on the Hundred Chart.

You may also wish to model a sample Secret Number activity with the entire class. Choose four students from different groups. Give each student a clue card from **Secret Number–A**. Choose a fifth student to work with a large Hundred Chart in the front of the room or a small Chart at the overhead projector. Distribute a Fifty or Hundred chart to each student. Have one student read her clue card, ("The number is greater than 20"). Ask the class what numbers are eliminated by this clue (1–20) and have them cross out these numbers on their charts. Proceed with each of the other three clues. Stop several times to ask students why a particular number has been eliminated. Be sure to emphasize that once a number is crossed out, it cannot be used, even if it fits another clue, for example, the number "18" has already been eliminated by the first clue. It cannot be re-used when a new clue states that "you get to the number when you count by 2's").

Other Logistics

It may be helpful to point out that some clues eliminate many numbers (for example, the number has a 3 in it) and others eliminate fewer numbers (for example, the number is greater than 10). Groups may find that if they first read all four clues, they can better determine which clue to use first. Students will also need to decide who will record the clues on the Hundred Chart. The chart can move from student to student as each clue is read. Then, the reader of the clue becomes the recorder of the information. The recorder can also be a designated person in the group or a fifth person (if the group has an extra member). Then, a new recorder can be selected for each activity.

ASSESSMENT

Have students color in a pattern on the Hundred Chart, name the pattern and describe it.

Give the students a list of clues. Have them use the clues to pinpoint a specific number, for example, "The number is less than 30. You get to the number if you count by 10's. The number has a 2 in the tens' place. What is the number?"

Give the students a number, for example, 15. Ask students to describe the number in as many ways as they can, for example, "It is odd. It has two digits. You get to the number if you count by 3's and 5's. There is a five in the ones' place."

GOING FURTHER

Number Search

Ask students to choose a number within an age-appropriate range (for example, one to ten for Grade 2) and list clues that will help a classmate guess the number. For example, if the number is 8, a student might write: "It is even. It is two more than six." Then, have students trade clues and search for numbers.

Name My Pattern

Have each student color in a pattern on the Hundred Chart. Then, ask students to trade patterns and try to name their classmates' patterns.

Number Facts

This activity does not use a Hundred Chart but will reinforce concepts from Secret Number activities. Have students find interesting number facts (within an age-appropriate range of numerals) from a textbook, almanac, encyclopedia or the *Guinness Book of World Records*. Ask them to create a series of clues that will help their classmates guess the number. For example, the longest jump by a flea was 13 inches. Appropriate clues for this fact would include: "The number has two digits. Both digits are odd. The digit in the ones' place is two more than the digit in the tens' place. The number is less than twenty."

The clues should narrow down the number to several possibilities. Classmates will then read the clues and make a reasonable guess that fits the information. After the guesses are reviewed and revised if necessary, the fact can be revealed.

Secret Number - A

The number is greater than 20.

Secret Number - A

The number is less than 40.

Secret Number - A

You get to the number if you count by 5's.

Secret Number - A

You get to the number if you count by 2's.

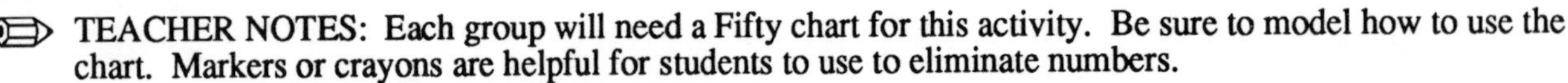

TEACHER NOTES: Each group will need a Fifty chart for this activity. Be sure to model how to use the chart. Markers or crayons are helpful for students to use to eliminate numbers.

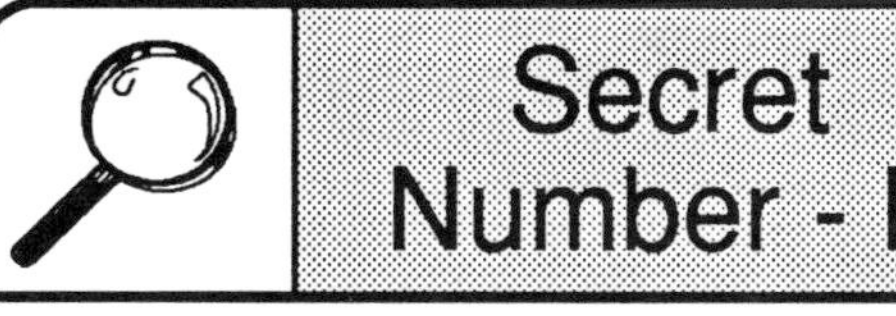

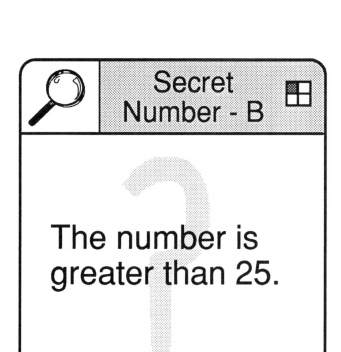

The number is greater than 25.

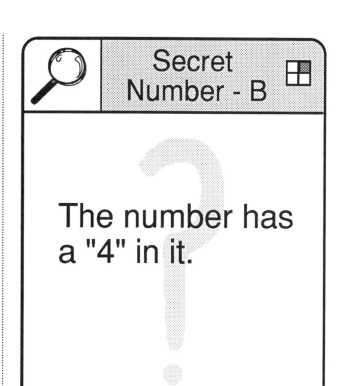

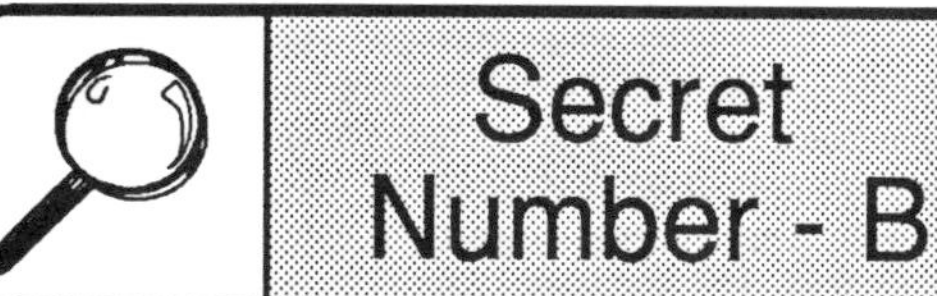

The number has a "4" in it.

The number has a "3" in it.

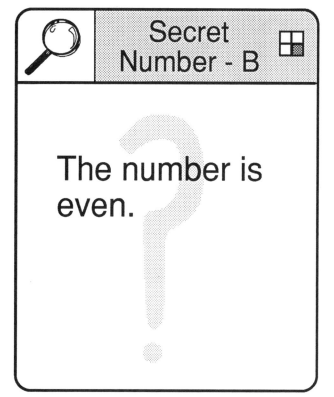

The number is even.

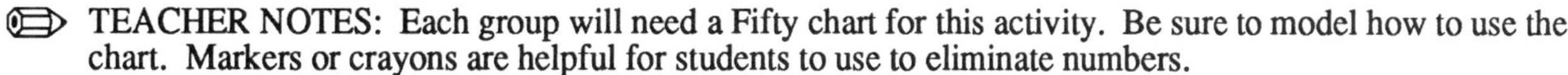

TEACHER NOTES: Each group will need a Fifty chart for this activity. Be sure to model how to use the chart. Markers or crayons are helpful for students to use to eliminate numbers.

Secret Number - C

The number is odd.

Secret Number - C

The number is greater than 10.

Secret Number - C

The number is less than 20.

Secret Number - C

You get to the number if you count by 5's.

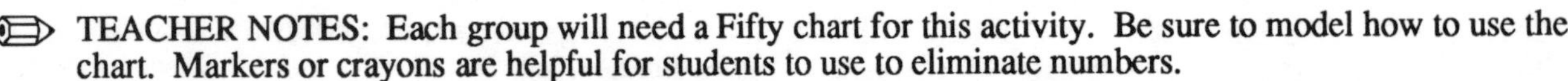

TEACHER NOTES: Each group will need a Fifty chart for this activity. Be sure to model how to use the chart. Markers or crayons are helpful for students to use to eliminate numbers.

Secret Number - D

The number is less than 80.

Secret Number - D

The number has two digits.

Secret Number - D

The digits in the number are the same.

Secret Number - D

If you add the digits, the sum is 12.

TEACHER NOTES: Each group will need a Hundred chart for this activity. Be sure to model how to use the chart. Markers or crayons are helpful for students to use to eliminate numbers. You may need to review the meaning of the word "digit" before students solve the problem.

Secret Number - E

You get to the number if you count by 5's.

Secret Number - E

The number is even.

Secret Number - E

The digit in the tens' place is larger than the digit in the ones' place.

Secret Number - E

If you add the digits, the sum is 5.

TEACHER NOTES: Each group will need a Hundred chart for this activity. Be sure to model how to use the chart. Markers or crayons are helpful for students to use to eliminate numbers. You may need to review the meaning of the word "digit" before students solve the problem.

Secret Number - F

You get to the number if you count by 10's.

Secret Number - F

The number is even.

Secret Number - F

You get to the number if you count by 20's.

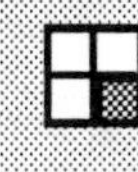

Secret Number - F

If you add the digits, the sum is 1.

 TEACHER NOTES: Each group will need a Hundred chart for this activity. Be sure to model how to use the chart. Markers or crayons are helpful for students to use to eliminate numbers. You may need to review the meaning of the word "digit" before students solve the problem.

Secret Number - G

The number is on the top half of the 100 chart.

Secret Number - G

The number is odd.

Secret Number - G

If you add the digits, the sum is 8.

Secret Number - G

The digit in the ones' place is 2 more than the digit in the tens' place.

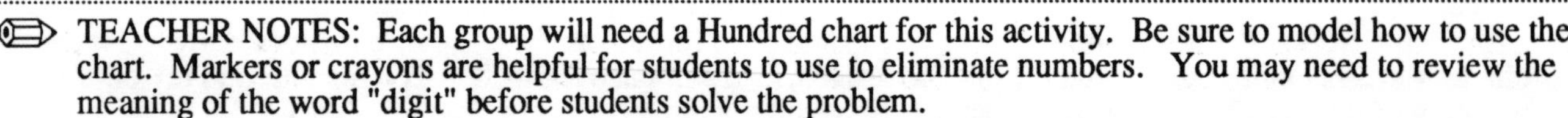

TEACHER NOTES: Each group will need a Hundred chart for this activity. Be sure to model how to use the chart. Markers or crayons are helpful for students to use to eliminate numbers. You may need to review the meaning of the word "digit" before students solve the problem.

Secret Number - H

The number is on the bottom half of the 100 chart.

Secret Number - H

The digit in the tens' place is even.

Secret Number - H

The digit in the ones' place is odd.

Secret Number - H

The sum of the digits is 17.

 TEACHER NOTES: Each group will need a Hundred chart for this activity. Be sure to model how to use the chart. Markers or crayons are helpful for students to use to eliminate numbers. You may need to review the meaning of the word "digit" before students solve the problem.

Fifty Chart

1	2	3	4	5	6	7	8	9	10
11	12	13	14	15	16	17	18	19	20
21	22	23	24	25	26	27	28	29	30
31	32	33	34	35	36	37	38	39	40
41	42	43	44	45	46	47	48	49	50

Fifty Chart

1	2	3	4	5	6	7	8	9	10
11	12	13	14	15	16	17	18	19	20
21	22	23	24	25	26	27	28	29	30
31	32	33	34	35	36	37	38	39	40
41	42	43	44	45	46	47	48	49	50

Hundred Chart

1	2	3	4	5	6	7	8	9	10
11	12	13	14	15	16	17	18	19	20
21	22	23	24	25	26	27	28	29	30
31	32	33	34	35	36	37	38	39	40
41	42	43	44	45	46	47	48	49	50
51	52	53	54	55	56	57	58	59	60
61	62	63	64	65	66	67	68	69	70
71	72	73	74	75	76	77	78	79	80
81	82	83	84	85	86	87	88	89	90
91	92	93	94	95	96	97	98	99	100

Coin Count

OVERVIEW

Students use a variety of coins as they work together on **COIN COUNT** activities. The clue cards direct younger children to place pennies, nickels and dimes in a cup. When all clues have been shared, these students can count the coins and find the total number of coins; the number of each type of coin and, if appropriate, the total value. Older children use the clues to figure out how much money "the kids" have. They may need to determine the distribution of coins and/or the total amount of money. Coin Count Recording Sheets are provided as a tool to keep track of students' solutions and progress.

The **COIN COUNT** family integrates well with mathematics units on Money.

Skills

- **Money:**
  Identification of coins
  Counting/place value
  Equivalence of coins
- Comparison of amounts
- Deductive reasoning
- Communication

Concepts and Vocabulary

- **Money:**
  penny, nickel, dime, quarter, coins
- **Numeration:**
  total, add, more than, same number of, how much in all, twice as many, two more

	Suggested Grade Levels					
Activity	K	1	2	3	4	5
Coin Count 1–5	✓	✓	✓			
Coin Count 6		✓	✓			
Coin Count 7			✓	✓		
Coin Count 8			✓	✓	✓	
Coin Count 9 and 10				✓	✓	
Coin Count 11 and 12				✓	✓	✓

GETTING READY

Each cooperative group will need a collection of real coins or authentic play money. Specific coins necessary for each activity are listed in the teacher notes. Sources for play money are listed on page 138. Half dollars are not used in these activities. For **Coin Count 1–6**, each group will need to place their coins in a cup, plastic plate or small transparent container.

You will need to color in the featured coins on the clue cards for **Coin Count 1–6** so that they resemble real money. This will make the coins recognizable for your students. We suggest that you color the coins before you cut up the clues.

You may wish to duplicate the **Coin Count Recording Sheet** (see page 110) on white paper to be used for assessment in Grades 2–4 (see Assessment section on page 97).

> ***OPTION:*** *Use a muffin tin, coin box or four-compartment container to sort and store collections of pennies, nickels, dimes and quarters for each group. You can label each section of the tin with a coin stamp or picture of an actual coin.*

INTRODUCTORY ACTIVITIES

Coin Collections

Grades K–1

Give each student a penny and a magnifying glass. Ask students to look closely at the coin and describe it in as much detail as they can, for example: "It is a penny. It is copper. It has a man on it. There is a different picture on the front and the back of each coin." Introduce a nickel, dime and quarter in the same manner.

Grades 1–4

Have each group sort a collection of coins into several cups or yarn loops. After the coins are sorted, ask groups to report about the content and value of their collection. Begin with simple collections (for example, three pennies, one nickel and two dimes) and then increase the number and type of coins, as appropriate to the level of your students. Line up the collections according to their value and compare them. Older students can explore the question, "Do the collections with the largest number of coins also have the highest values?"

Rolling For Riches

This game helps children count one type of coin. Have students work in partners with one die and a collection of pennies, nickels, dimes or quarters. Students take turns rolling the die. The die indicates the number of coins that they will collect (for example, if they roll a 2, they take two coins). The game ends after each student has rolled the die five times. Then, total up the coins to see who has the most (or least) money. Students may also begin with a fixed number of coins (for example, 20 dimes), and have them "spend" money according to the roll of the die.

Coin Combinations

Provide time for your students to practice trading coins for other coins of equal value. For example, ask students to discover how many different ways they can make 10¢, 25¢, or one dollar. Ask students to draw, write about or chart their solutions.

Coin Calendar

To provide daily practice with equivalent coins, have students use a variety of combinations of coins to total today's date. For example, on September 12, students can make 12¢ with 12 pennies; 1 dime and 2 pennies; 2 nickels and 2 pennies; or 1 nickel and 7 pennies.

TIPS FOR TEACHERS

Logistics

Coins are an appealing manipulative to most students. It would be worthwhile to discuss how the coins can be shared in the group. Common coin-sharing methods developed by students include: distribution of one type of coin to each student in the group (for example, one child is in charge of the pennies); selection of one coin counter (or "bank teller") to move the coins; or a rule that you can touch the coins only at the time when you read your clue card.

Grades K–1

It is essential to provide time for students to recognize, sort and count coins before you proceed with Coin Count logic problems. These activities are best used at the end of a unit on money. Young children will have more success with **COIN COUNT** if they have already worked on money values and concepts.

You may wish to model **Coin Count 1** with the entire class before they work in small groups. To do this, enlarge copies of the clues so that they are visible for all students. Distribute one clue to each of four children. Select one child to be the coin counter and give her at least 20 pennies (real coins or actual size or large authentic play money).

Have one student read one clue and then go to the coin counter to get the appropriate number of pennies. Ask the class to count the pennies, one by one, with the coin counter. The pennies should be counted again as they placed in a cup (or in a pocket chart). Have students read the other three cards, one at a time. Then, ask students to estimate the total number of coins in the cup. Then, count the total number of coins. At a later date, you may wish to distinguish between the number of coins (for example, 5 nickels) and the total amount of money (25¢). Before you distribute Coin Count problems to each group, be sure to emphasize that all the clue cards show the number of coins to put in the cup. In other words, some children will have clue cards with more coins than other students. These children are not "wealthier" because the coins in the cup ultimately belong to the entire group!

Grades 2–4

It is important to explore monetary equivalences (for example, 3 dimes are 30¢; two nickels equal the value of one dime) so that students can more easily solve **Coin Count 7–12** which are the more difficult activities in this family. (See **Coin Combinations** in the introductory activities).

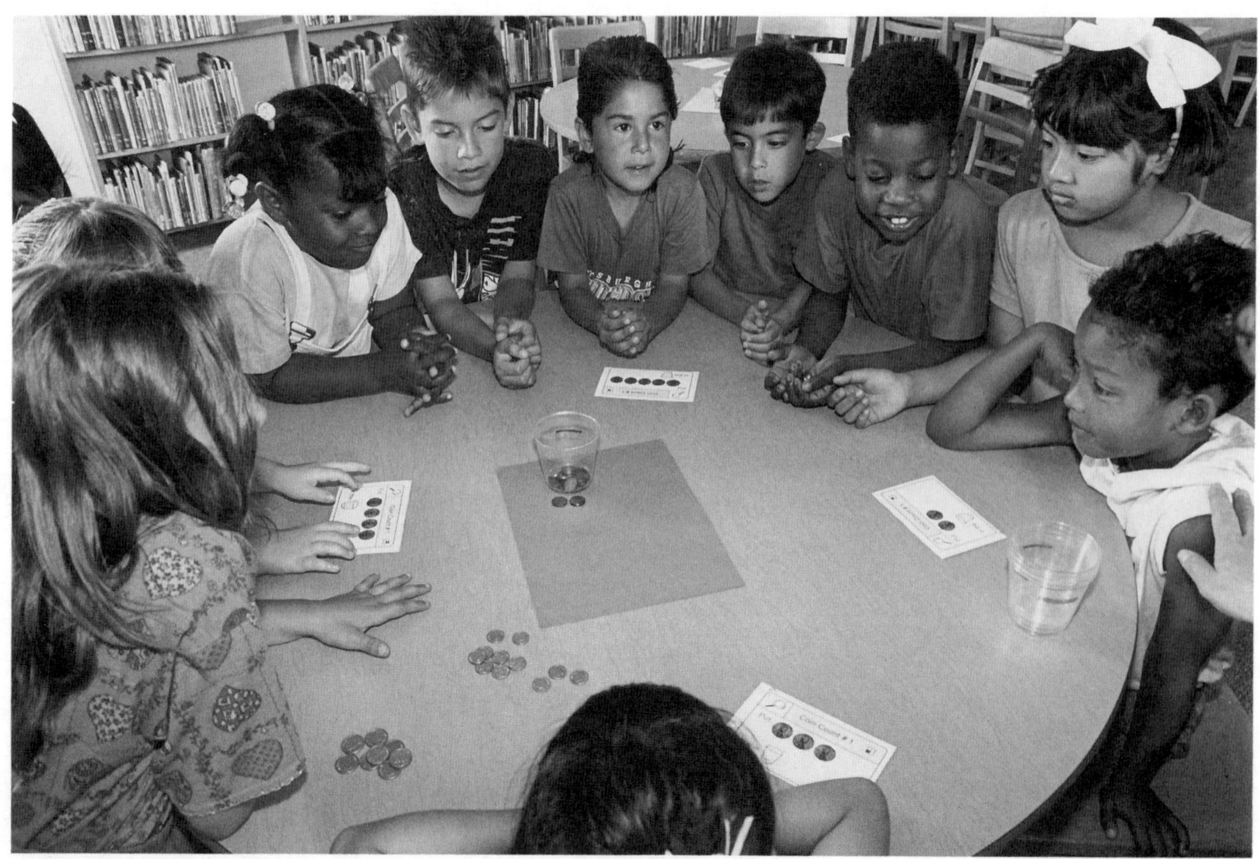

ASSESSMENT

Grades K–1

Ask each student to record their group's solution in pictures or with coin stamps as a recording tool. You can also ask individual or pairs of students to use coins and design their own collection. They can then draw or stamp the collection and write its total value.

Grades 2–4

Ask each student to record their group's solution on a Coin Count Recording Sheet (see pages 110-111). Or, you can ask students to design their own chart to depict their solution.

GOING FURTHER

Art Store

Set up a mini-store with an assortment of materials for an art project. Place the materials in boxes and label each box with a price, (for example, Straws = 1¢). Give each student a grade-appropriate budget of coins to "spend" on supplies for the art project. Provide time for students to visit the store and purchase supplies for the project. The store can be staffed by students or adults.

Kids in Business

Have students create a restaurant or store and design a menu or price list. Older students can develop word problems to go with their projects.

Smart Shoppers

Collect advertising flyers from a local supermarket. Distribute the flyers to your students. Have them explore the flyers and make statements about what they've found. You can also assign specific tasks, for example: "Find an item that you can eat for less than $1.00. Find the item with the highest price. Work with a partner to plan a balanced meal for $10." If calculators are available, encourage students to use them during the activity.

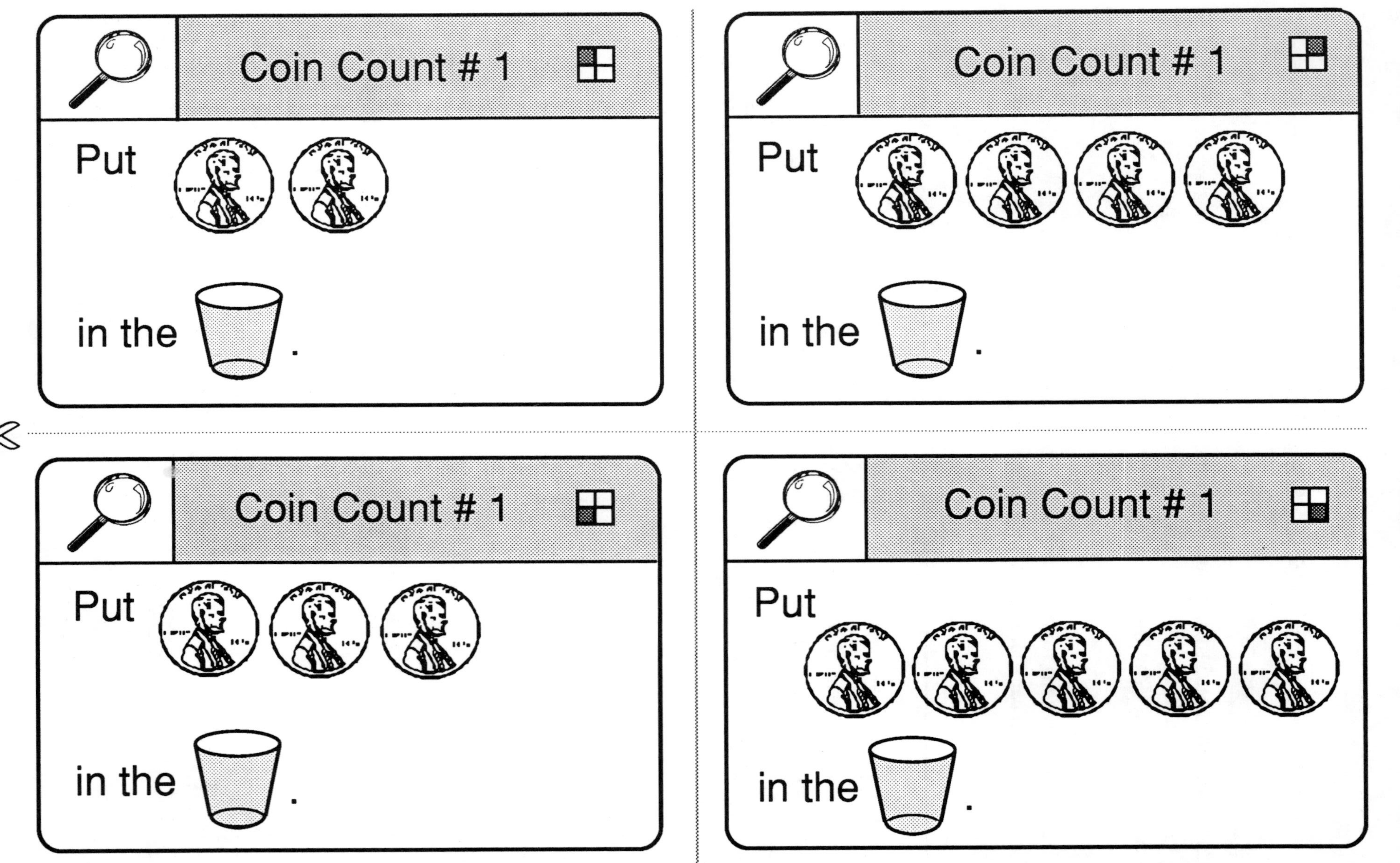

TEACHER NOTES: Duplicate this page on white card stock. Color the coins on the clue cards so they resemble real coins. Each group will need one cup and 20 pennies. Tell the students to follow their clue cards and place coins in the cup. Then, they should count the total number of coins and/or the value of the money in the cup, as appropriate.

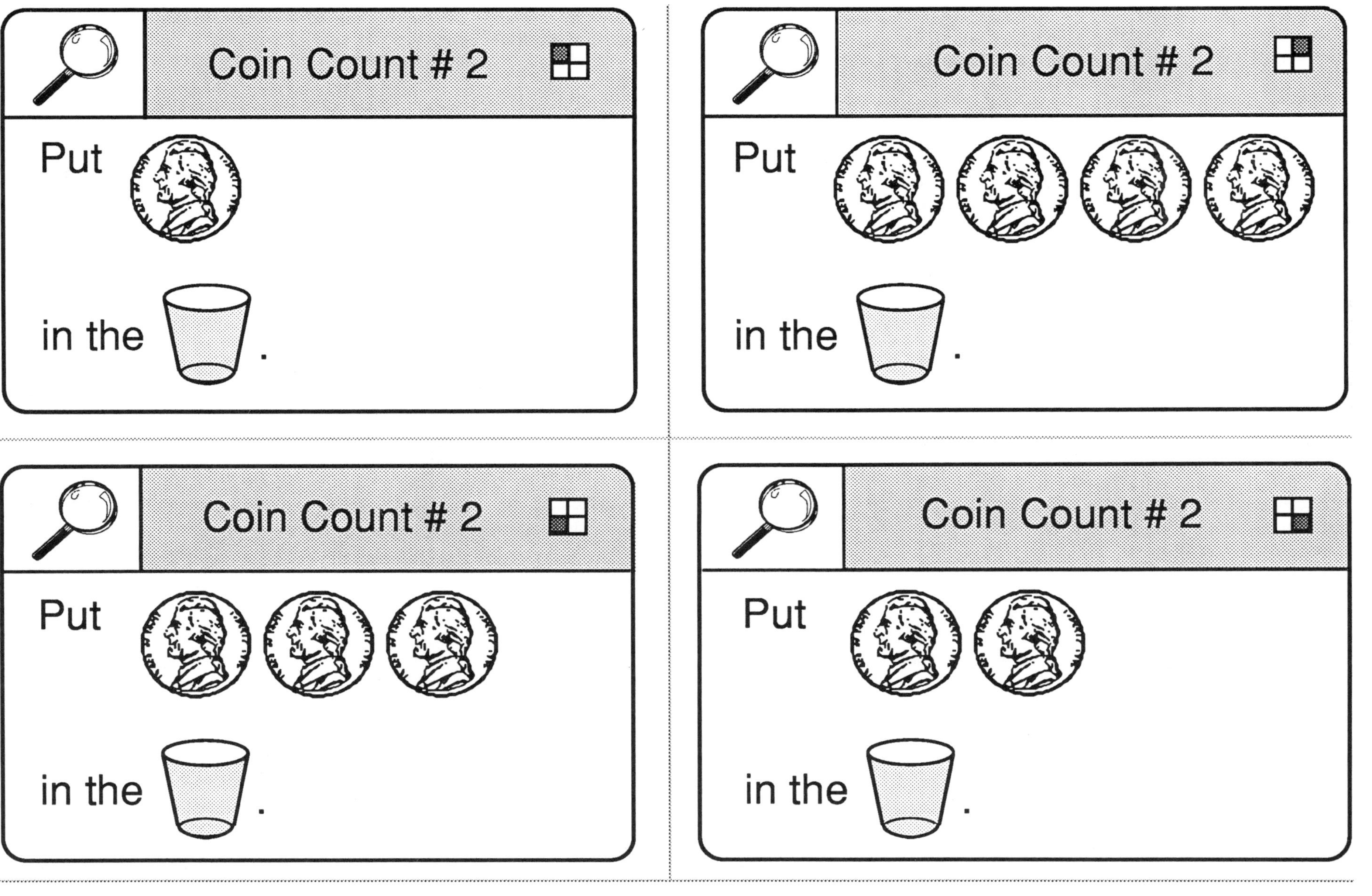

TEACHER NOTES: Duplicate this page on white card stock. Color the coins on the clue cards so they resemble real coins. Each group will need one cup and 15 nickels. Tell the students to follow their clue cards and place coins in the cup. Then, they should count the total number of coins and/or the value of the money in the cup, as appropriate.

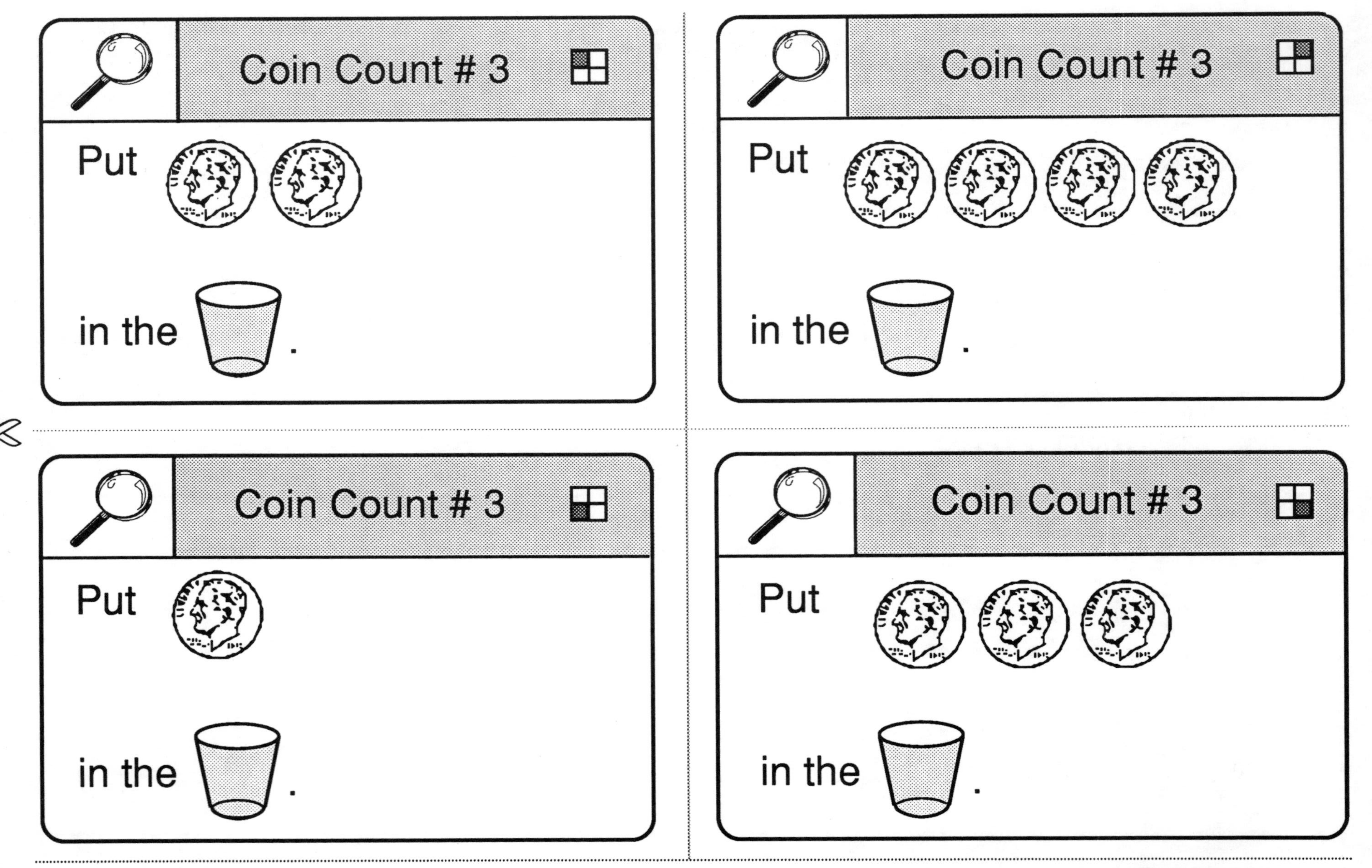

TEACHER NOTES: Duplicate this page on white card stock. Color the coins on the clue cards so they resemble real coins. Each group will need one cup and 15 dimes. Tell the students to follow their clue cards and place coins in the cup. Then, they should count the total number of coins and/or the value of the money in the cup, as appropriate.

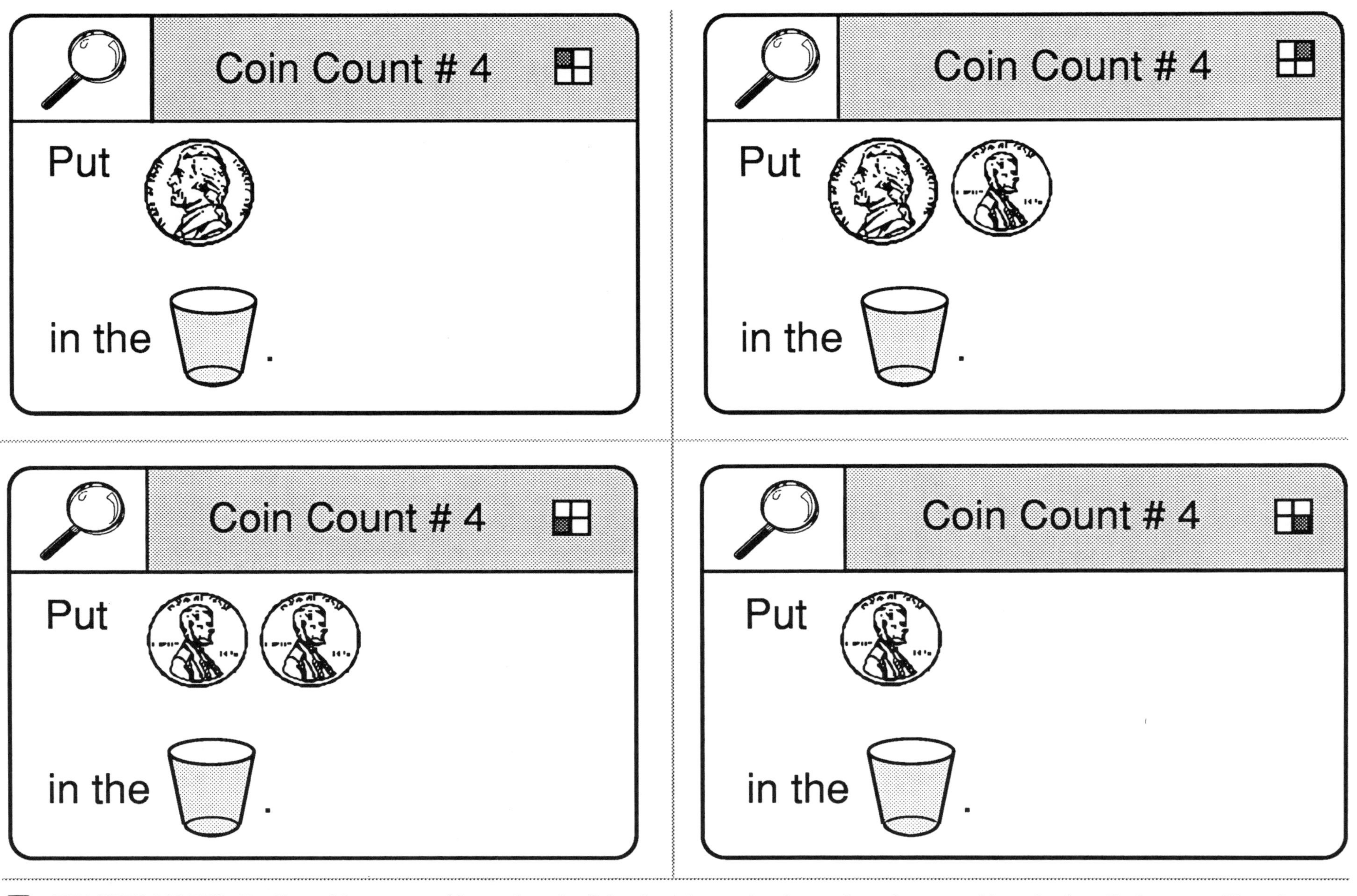

TEACHER NOTES: Duplicate this page on white card stock. Color the coins on the clue cards so they resemble real coins. Each group will need one cup, 10 pennies and 5 nickels. Tell the students to follow their clue cards and place coins in the cup. Then, they should count the total number of coins and/or the value of the money in the cup, as appropriate.

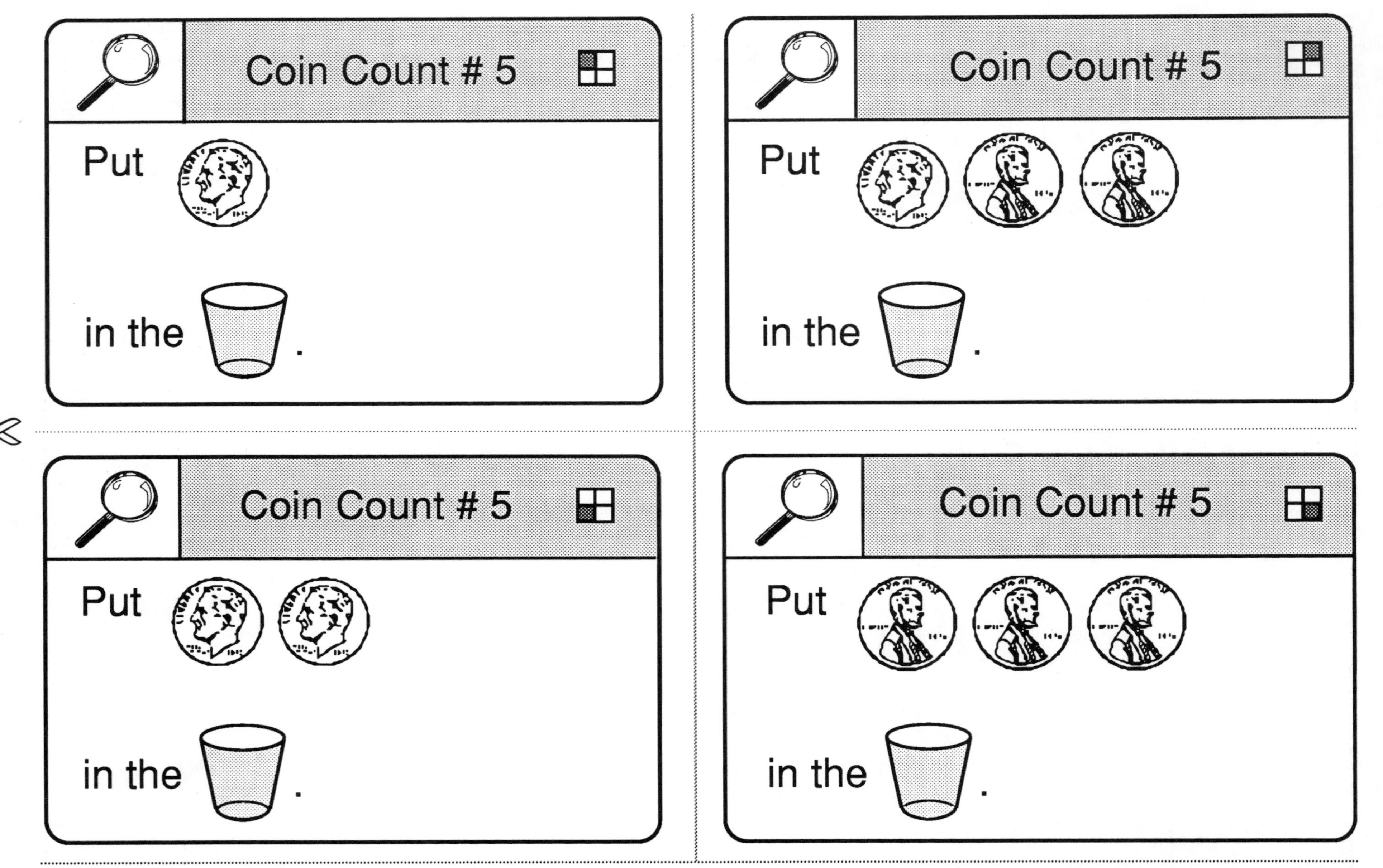

TEACHER NOTES: Duplicate this page on white card stock. Color the coins on the clue cards so they resemble real coins. Each group will need one cup, 10 pennies and 5 dimes. Tell the students to follow their clue cards and place coins in the cup. Then, they should count the total number of coins and/or the value of the money in the cup, as appropriate.

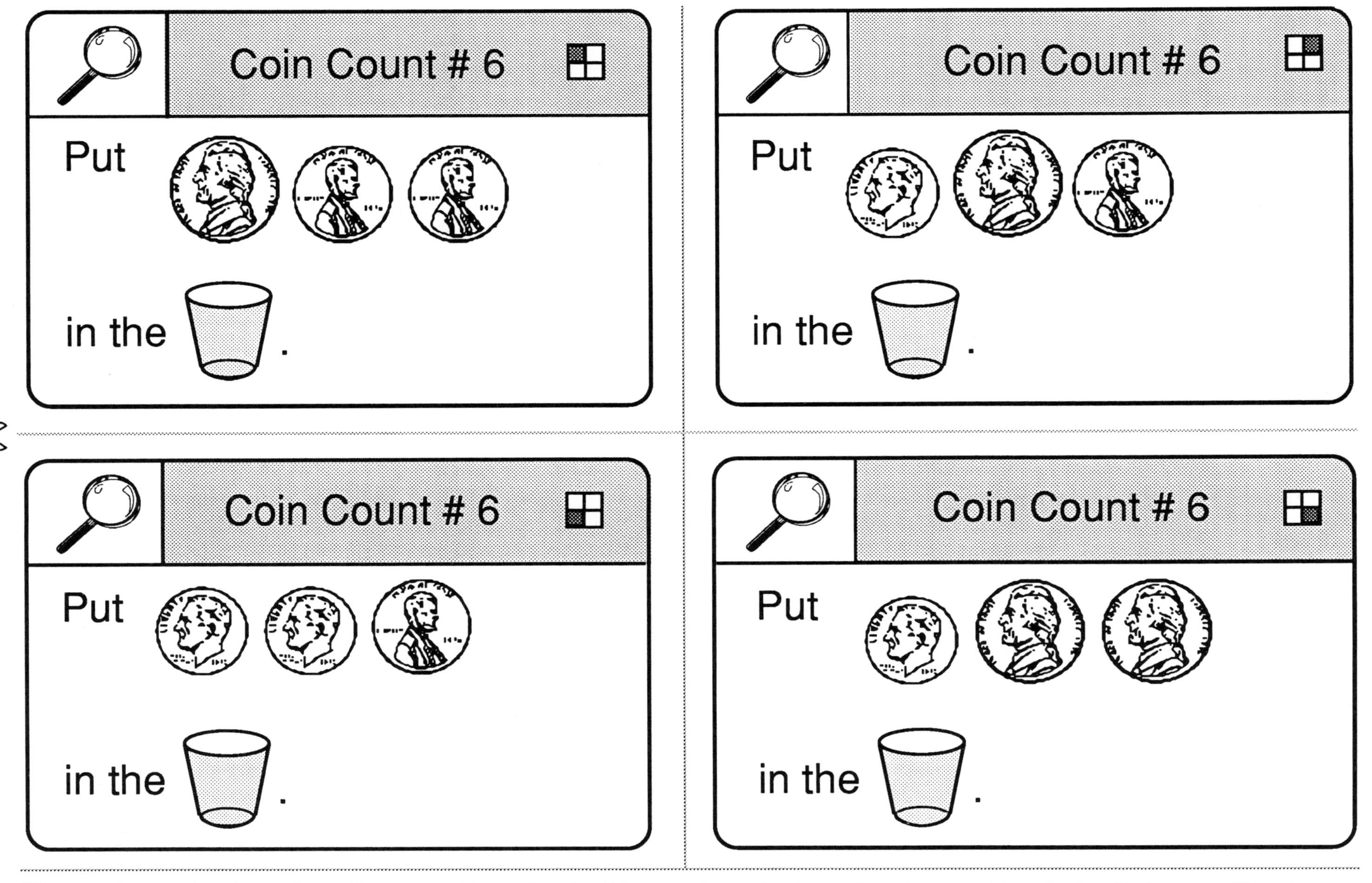

TEACHER NOTES: Duplicate this page on white card stock. Color the coins on the clue cards so they resemble real coins. Each group will need one cup, 5 pennies, 5 nickels and 5 dimes. Tell the students to follow their clue cards and place coins in the cup. Then, they should count the total number of coins and/or the value of the money in the cup, as appropriate.

Coin Count
7

The kids have
1 quarter.

Count all the
money.

Coin Count
7

The kids have
30¢ in dimes.

Count all the
money.

Coin Count
7

The kids have
5 nickels.

Count all the
money.

Coin Count
7

The kids have
the same number
of pennies as
nickels.

Count all the
money.

TEACHER NOTES: Each group of students will need an assortment of at least ten pennies, nickels, dimes and quarters. Students should use the clues to find the total number of coins and/or the value of coins.

Coin Count
8

The kids have 11 coins.

Count all the money.

Coin Count
8

The kids have pennies, nickels and dimes.

Count all the money.

Coin Count
8

The kids have three nickels.

Count all the money.

Coin Count
8

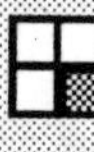

The kids have the same number of dimes and pennies.

Count all the money.

TEACHER NOTES: Each group of students will need an assortment of at least ten pennies, nickels, dimes and quarters. Students should use the clues to find the total number of coins and/or the value of coins.

Coin Count
9

The kids have as many pennies as the number of legs on an insect.

Count all the money.

Coin Count
9

If you add the number of dimes and pennies, you get the number of legs on an octopus.

Count all the money.

Coin Count
9

The kids have as many quarters as the number of legs on a dog.

Count all the money.

Coin Count
9

If you put all the nickels, dimes and quarters in your hand, you will have nine coins.

Count all the money.

TEACHER NOTES: Each group of students will need an assortment of at least ten pennies, nickels, dimes and quarters. Students should use the clues to find the total number of coins and/or the value of coins.

Coin Count
 # 10

The kids have a total of $1.00 in coins.

Which coins do they have?

Coin Count
 # 10

The kids have two dimes.

Which coins do they have?

Coin Count
 # 10

All of the kids' coins are silver in color.

Which coins do they have?

Coin Count
 # 10

If you add the kids' dimes and nickels, the total is 25¢.

Which coins do they have?

 TEACHER NOTES: Each group of students will need an assortment of at least ten pennies, nickels, dimes and quarters. Students should use the clues to determine exactly which coins the kids have.

Coin Count
11

The kids have a total of $1.56.

Which coins do they have?

Coin Count
11

The kids have 16 coins in all.

Which coins do they have?

Coin Count
11

The kids have twice as many dimes as nickels.

Which coins do they have?

Coin Count
11

The kids have two more pennies than quarters.

Which coins do they have?

 TEACHER NOTES: Each group of students will need an assortment of at least ten pennies, nickels, dimes and quarters. Students should use the clues to determine exactly which coins the kids have.

Coin Count # 12

Kimi and Maria have 12 coins in all.

Which coins does each kid have?

Coin Count # 12

Maria has 59¢.

Which coins does each kid have?

Coin Count # 12

Kimi has 41¢ more than Maria.

Which coins does each kid have?

Coin Count # 12

Maria has twice as many coins as Kimi.

Which coins does each kid have?

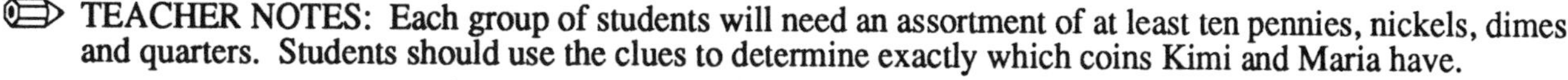

TEACHER NOTES: Each group of students will need an assortment of at least ten pennies, nickels, dimes and quarters. Students should use the clues to determine exactly which coins Kimi and Maria have.

Coin Count Recording Sheet

Name(s) ______________________________

COIN COUNT #	quarters	dimes	nickels	pennies	TOTAL MONEY

Coin Count Recording Sheet

Name(s) ____

COIN COUNT #	quarters	dimes	nickels	pennies	TOTAL MONEY

N
W
E
S
GEMS
Lawrence Hall of Science
University of California
Berkeley, CA 94720

ARE BEST FRIENDS

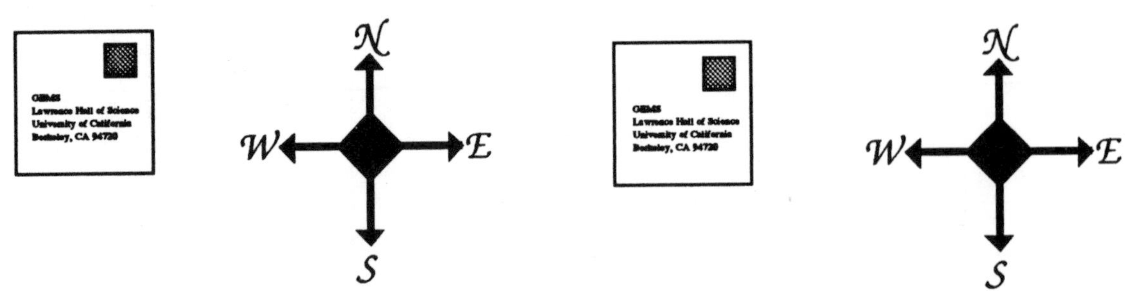
GEMS
Lawrence Hall of Science
University of California
Berkeley, CA 94720
N
W
E
S

Maps

OVERVIEW

The activities in **MAPS** provide an opportunity to integrate mathematics and social studies concepts. Students in each cooperative group share one map of **Bear Park, Bear Street** and **Cubeville** for hands-on map reading and problem solving. The **Bear Park Map** is designed for young children and beginning readers. On **Bear Street**, students place plastic bears at specific locations and addresses and begin to explore basic compass directions. The **Cubeville Map** introduces the compass rose (a picture which indicates the directional points on a compass) and a map legend. After they solve the problems, groups may decide to write stories about their bear and cube adventures!

Skills

- **Map reading:**
  - Finding specific locations
  - Directionality
  - Use of map legend
  - Use of compass rose
- Deductive reasoning
- Communication

Concepts and Vocabulary

- **Colors:** red, yellow, blue, green, orange
- **Directions**: below, above, between, next to, outside, next door, on top of, farthest, corner of, north (of), south (of), east (of), west (of)
- **Locations**: map, street, hill, lane, town square
- **Map terms**: legend, compass rose.

	Suggested Grade Levels					
Activity	K	1	2	3	4	5
Bear Park 1–6	✓	✓	✓			
Bear Park 7 and 8		✓	✓			
Bear Street 1 and 2			✓	✓	✓	
Bear Street 3 and 4				✓	✓	
Cubeville Map 1				✓	✓	
Cubeville Map 2–4					✓	✓

GETTING READY

For **Bear Park** and **Bear Street**, each group will need a collection of at least four plastic bears in each of the following colors: red, blue, yellow and green. If plastic bears are not available, duplicate the **Bear Line-Up Manipulatives** on page 75 on colored paper to create paper bears.

Groups who use the **Cubeville Map** will need a box or bag of seven wood cubes in each of the following colors: red, blue, yellow, green and orange. If cubes are not available, you can create paper squares in the five colors if you duplicate the graph paper on page 137.

For all activities, groups will need **one copy** of the **Bear Park, Bear Street** or **Cubeville** maps. Keep the maps unfolded so that bears and cubes can be placed on them. Encourage students to move their seats so that they all view the map from the same direction. Larger copies of the maps are found in the Appendix beginning on page 145. These can be duplicated on 11" x 17" paper and will be easier for groups of students to see.

> ***OPTION:*** *Make large drawings of the maps so that you can post them in the classroom and refer to them during the activities. If you laminate the maps or cover them with contact paper, they will be more durable.*

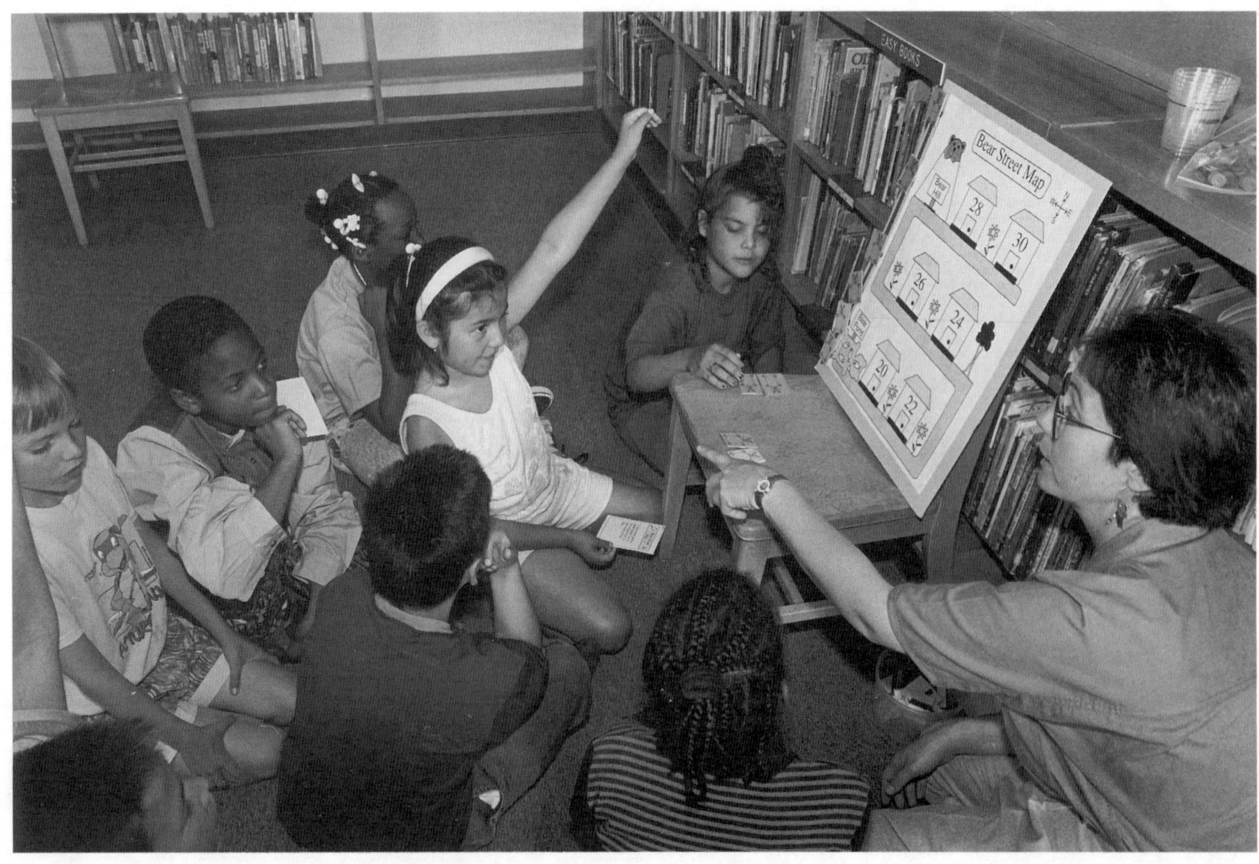

INTRODUCTORY ACTIVITIES

School Maps

Have the students make a variety of two and three-dimensional maps of the classroom or school building. Begin with a map of their group's table or desks. You can then move to a seating chart; a room map that features furniture; a playground map or a map of the principal's office. For a homework assignment, students can map a room in their home.

Map a Journey

Distribute pre-made maps to students as they go on a tour of the school, neighborhood or field trip site. Ask students to trace their path on the map during the excursion or when they return to the classroom. After the paths are mapped, have students write or orally describe the journeys. Encourage them to use key vocabulary appropriate to their grade level.

Free Exploration

Before you use a particular map for cooperative logic, duplicate it on white paper and distribute it to each student. Allow ample time for students to explore the map and offer observations and conclusions. You may wish to provide markers or crayons so that students can color the map to make it their own. Be sure to have students describe the map and discuss its key features (for example, streets, corners, the compass rose).

TIPS FOR TEACHERS

All Grades

Encourage students to sit on one side of the map so that it is oriented in the same direction for each group member. Then, the entire group will see the map from the same perspective.

Grades K–2

Students at this level will need to work with a variety of maps so they can begin to understand how an actual area or location can be represented on a two-dimensional drawing. The introductory activities in this section will help children make these connections. Free exploration of the specific maps for each activity is essential.

You may wish to demonstrate a Bear Park activity with your students before they work in small groups. Post an enlarged copy of the **Bear Park Map** and some pictures of red, blue, green and yellow bears in the front of the room. Distribute a copy of the map and a handful of bears to each student. Have students point to the landmarks on the map (flowers, pond, swings, tree). Then, give simple oral directions ("Put two bears on the swings") as to where to place the bears on the map. Have a volunteer tape bears on the large map according to your directions while students put bears on their maps at their seats. After students become familiar with the map, distribute the four clues from **Bear Park Map-1** to four students, one clue per student. Have each student share a clue with the class, and then place bears on the map as directed by the clue. Ask the class to confirm that the placement is correct. Explore a variety of interpretations of the clues. For example, the two bears on the swings can be of any color, so students' maps are likely to differ. Yet, they all are correct.

Grades 2–4

Bear Street and **Cubeville** maps require students to apply a variety of map concepts. You may need to review these concepts, particularly in the context of each map. You may also need to help students work out a system to share and place the bears and cubes on the map. As they place manipulatives on the map, students may need assistance to be sure that the top of the map faces north.

With Cubeville activities, students use six clues (rather than four) to place cubes on the map. You might wish to discuss this change before proceeding. Students will need to make an agreement about how to distribute the six clues equitably.

ASSESSMENT

Grades K–2

Have each student record their group's solution on a copy of the **Bear Park** or **Bear Street** map. Students can draw bears or use the **Bear Line-Up Manipulatives** (see "Getting Ready").

Grades 2–4

Have each student record their group's solution on a copy of the **Bear Street** or **Cubeville** map. For **Bear Street**, students can draw bears or use the bear manipulatives featured at the end of the Bear Line-Up section. For **Cubeville,** students can color the small squares on the map to represent the actual cubes. They can also paste pre-cut squares that are the colors of cubes on the map. In addition, students can make and label their own maps for the bears!

GOING FURTHER

Where Do You Live?

Contact your local planning commission or chamber of commerce to obtain a large street map of your town, school neighborhood or attendance area. Have students find where they live on the map and mark the location with their name, a symbol for a house or a small drawing. Students can then write their addresses in a class directory. Older students can compare the location of their home to their classmates' addresses, for example, "I live two blocks west of Jean's house."

Treasure Hunt

To reinforce the concept of North, South, East and West, group older students in pairs and give each student a sheet of graph paper with an **X** marked in the lower left hand corner. One student in each pair will color in one box on the grid to "hide" a treasure. This student should draw a path on her map from the **X** to the treasure. Her goal is to use compass directions to guide the second student, step by step, to the treasure. For example: "Go east two boxes. Go north three boxes."

The second student should mark each step on the map. When the treasure is found, partners should compare maps. If the directions were clear and accurately followed, the maps should be identical.

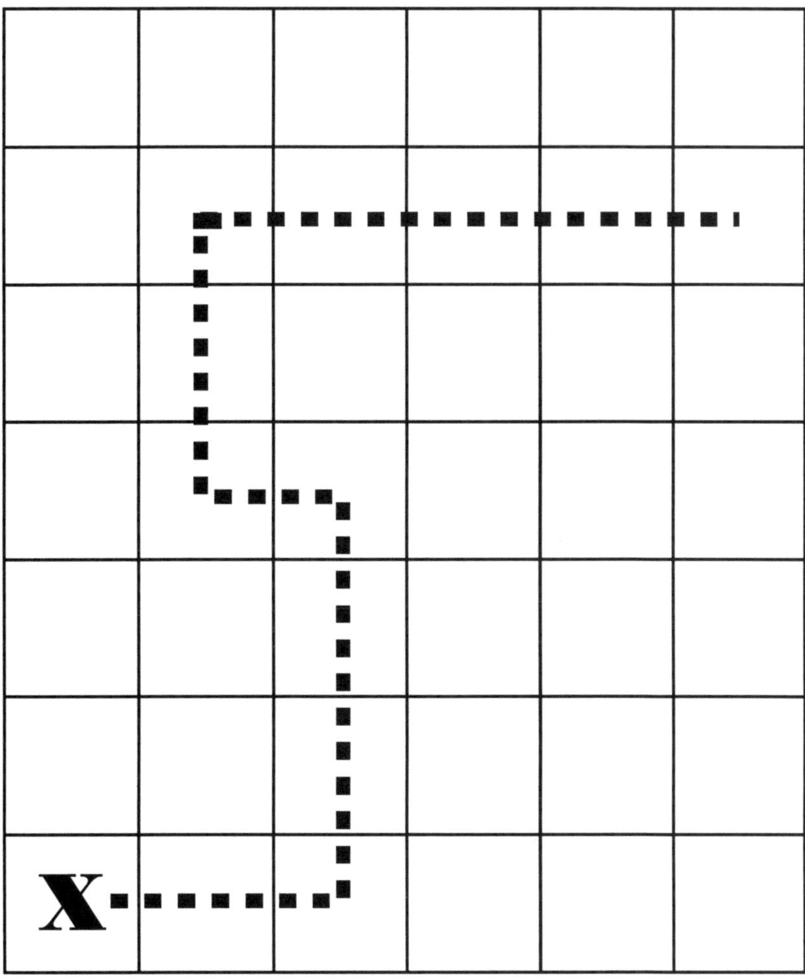

DIRECTIONS

Go **East** two boxes
Go **North** three boxes
Go **West** one box
Go **North** two boxes
Go **East** four boxes

Young Cartographers

Collect a variety of maps for students to explore and compare. Then, have students design their own map of an imaginary place (for example, a park, school, town, city or country). They can also write or dictate stories about their maps.

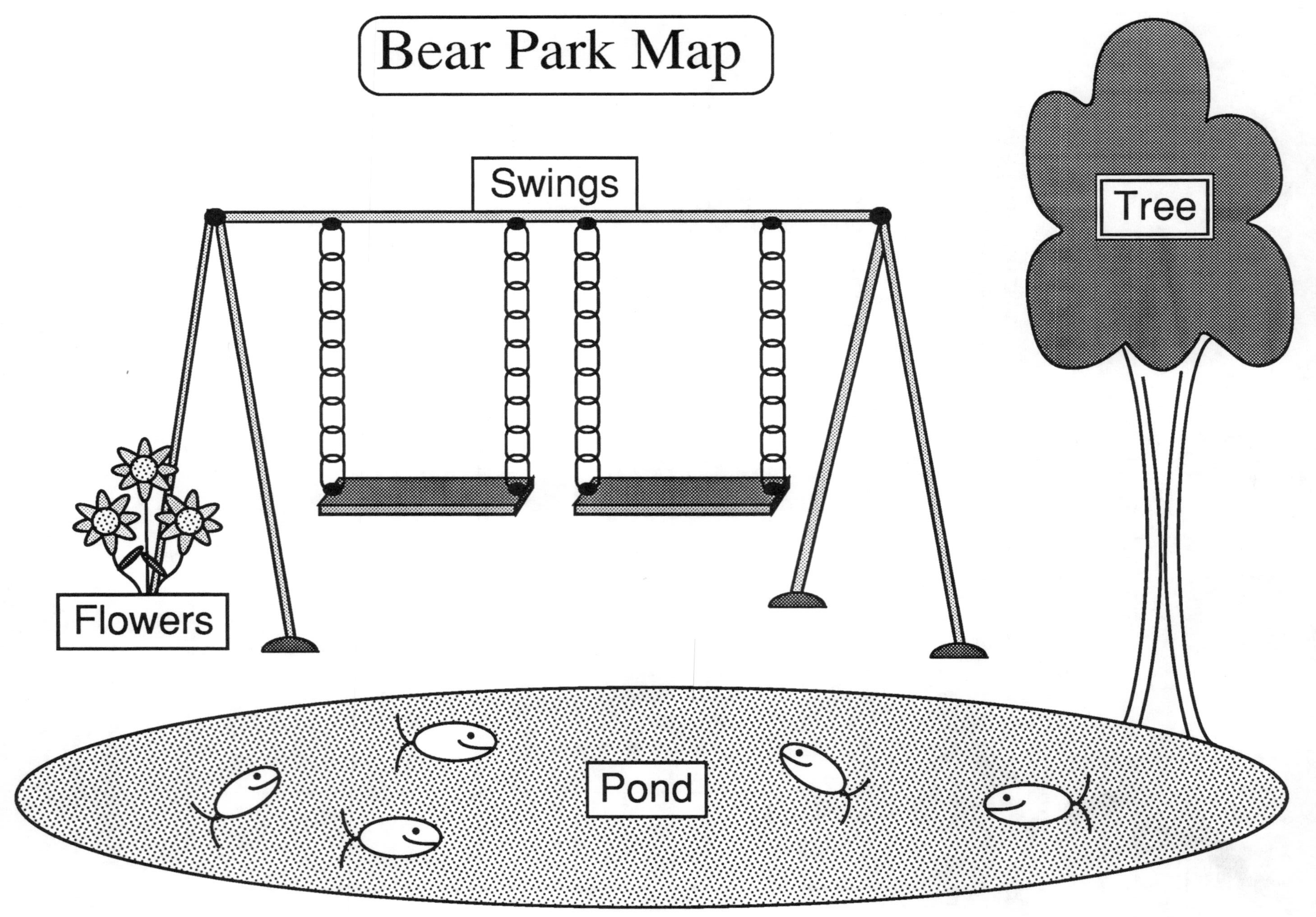
Bear Park Map
Swings
Tree
Flowers
Pond

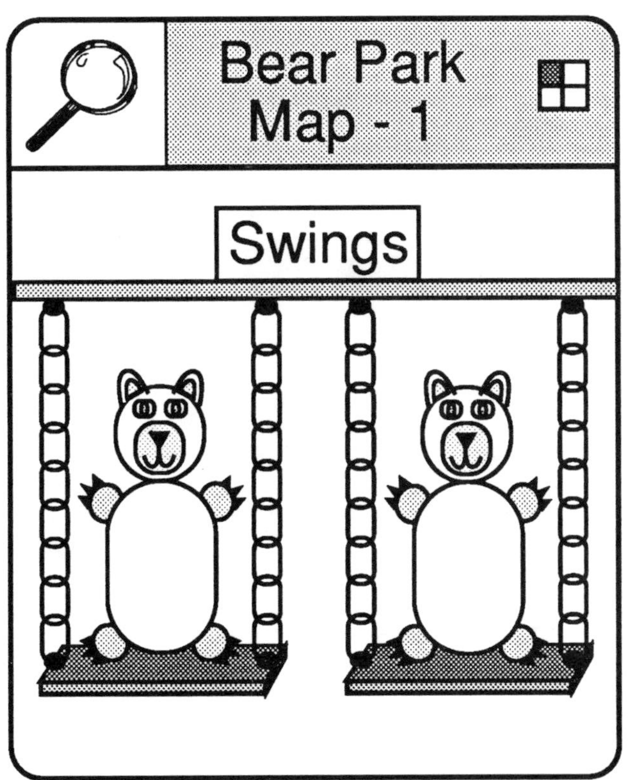

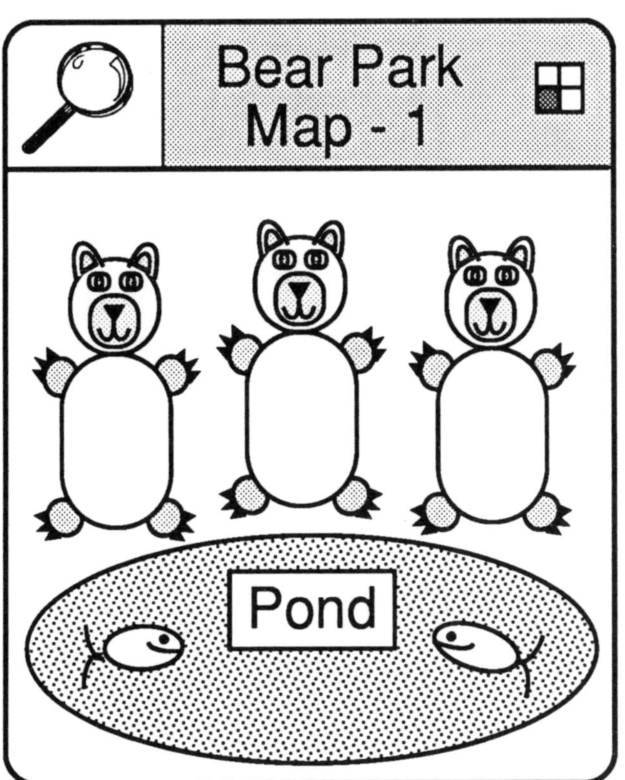

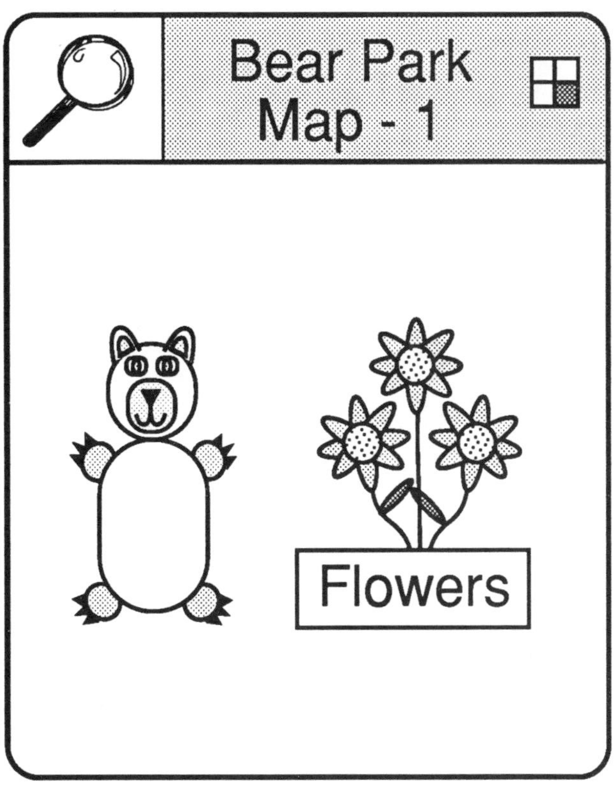

TEACHER NOTES: Each group will need a set of clue cards; one Bear Park map; and at least four bears in each of the following colors: red, blue, yellow and green. Explain to the students that they will use all four clues to place the bears on the map.

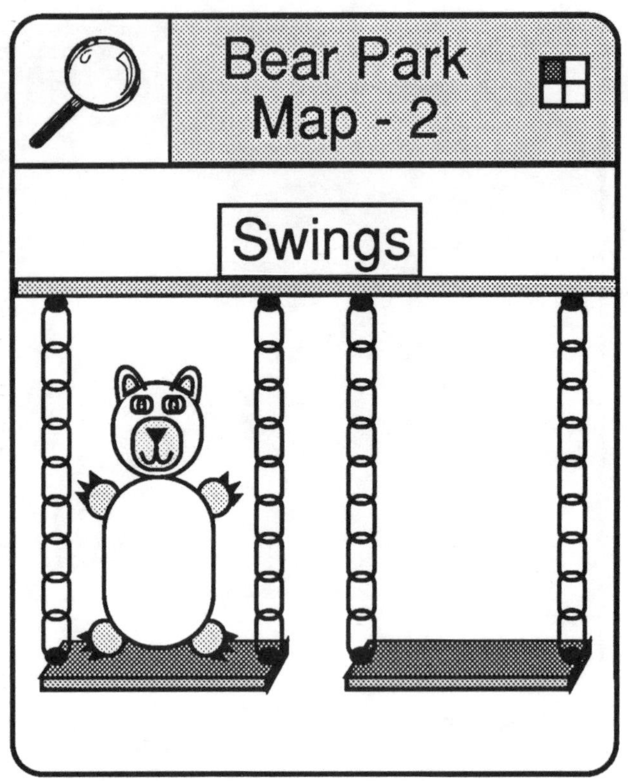

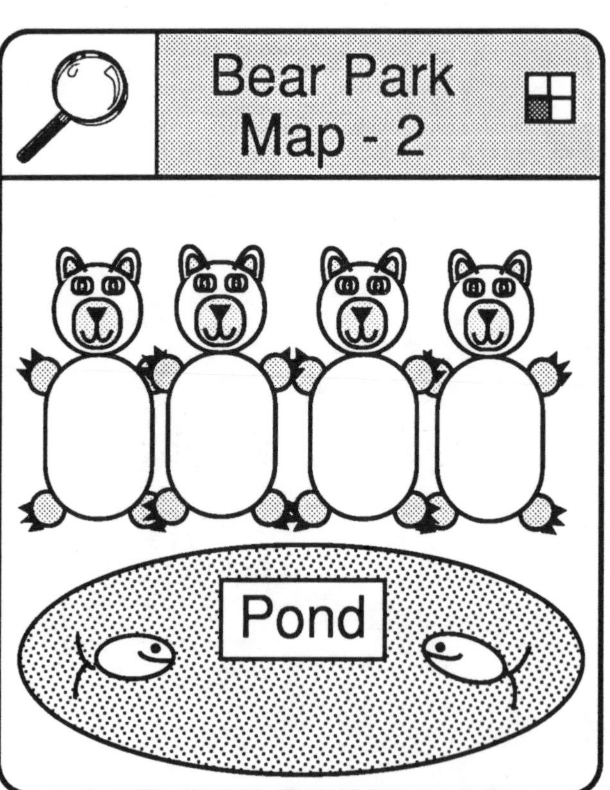

TEACHER NOTES: Each group will need a set of clue cards; one Bear Park map; and at least four bears in each of the following colors: red, blue, yellow and green. Explain to the students that they will use all four clues to place the bears on the map.

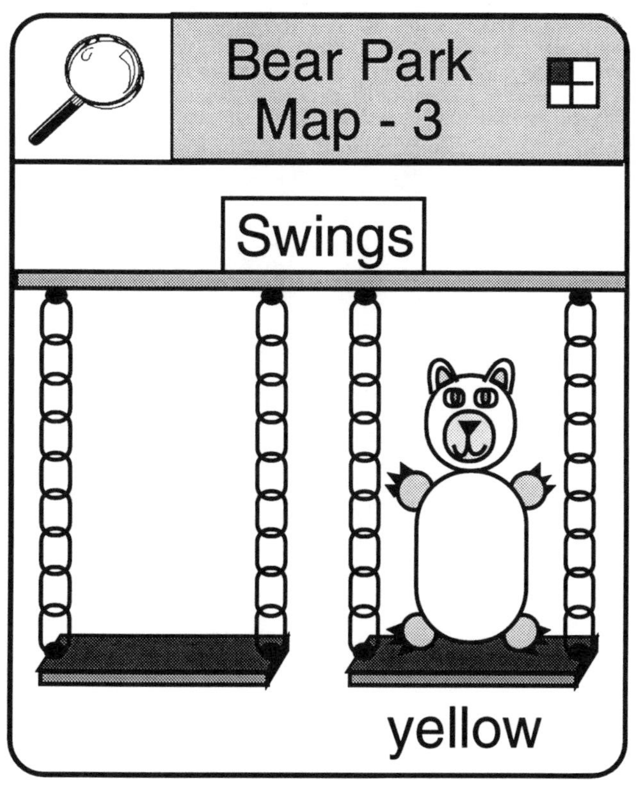

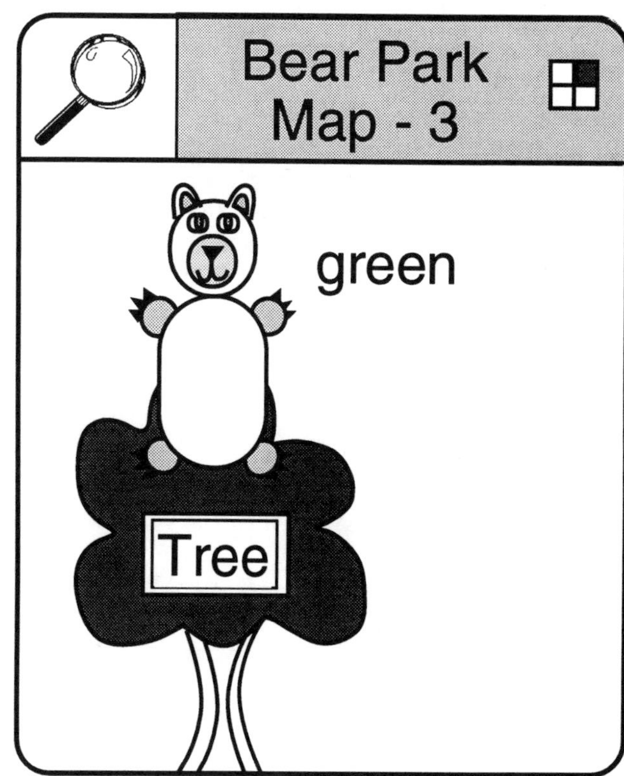

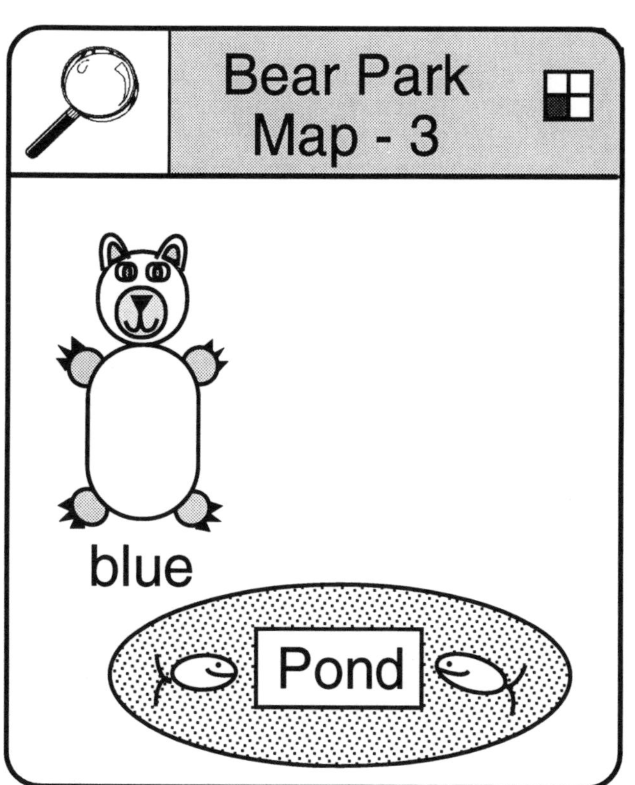

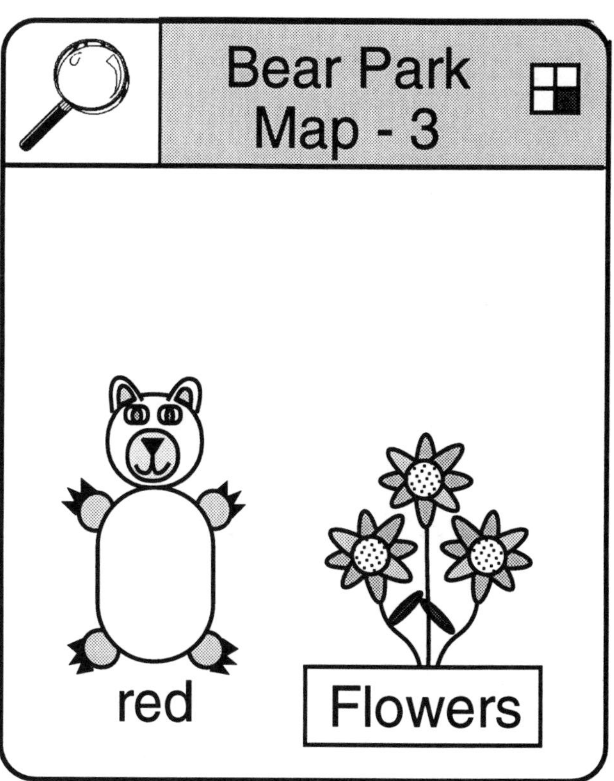

TEACHER NOTES: Each group will need a set of clue cards; one Bear Park map; and at least four bears in each of the following colors: red, blue, yellow and green. Explain to the students that they will use all four clues to place the bears on the map. You may wish to color in the featured bear/s on each clue card so that the color words will be easier for young children to read.

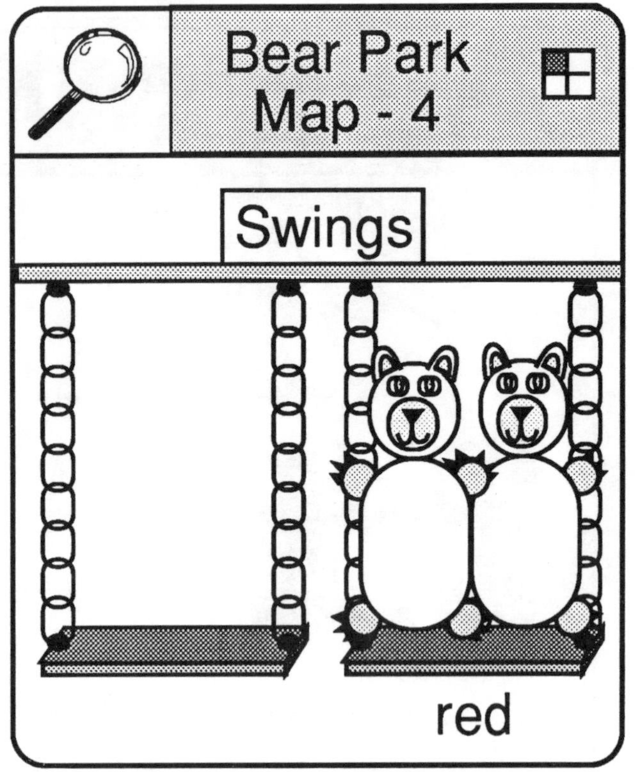

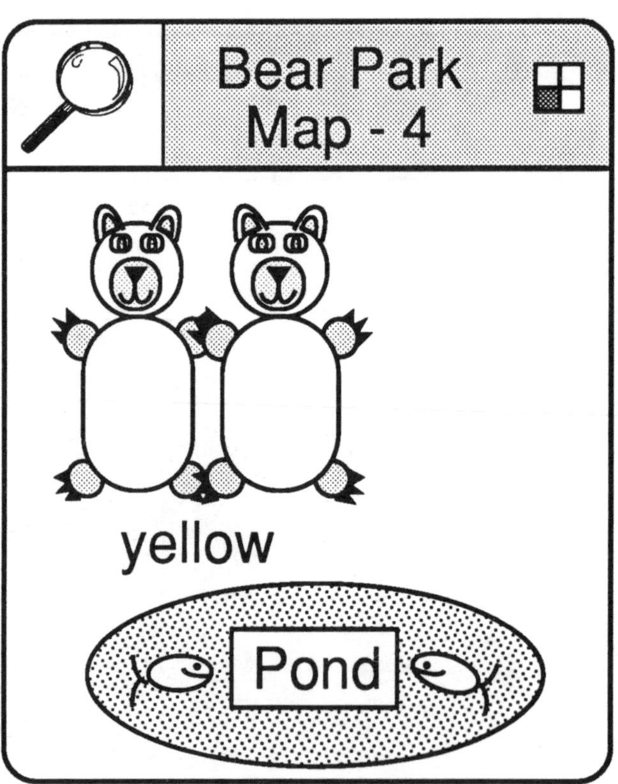

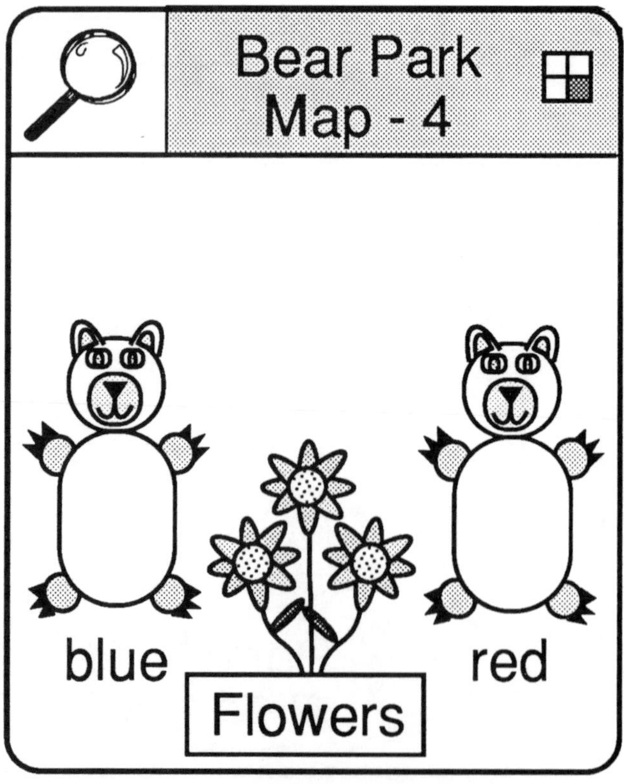

TEACHER NOTES: Each group will need a set of clue cards; one Bear Park map; and at least four bears in each of the following colors: red, blue, yellow and green. Explain to the students that they will use all four clues to place the bears on the map. You may wish to color in the featured bear/s on so that the color words will be easier for young children to read.

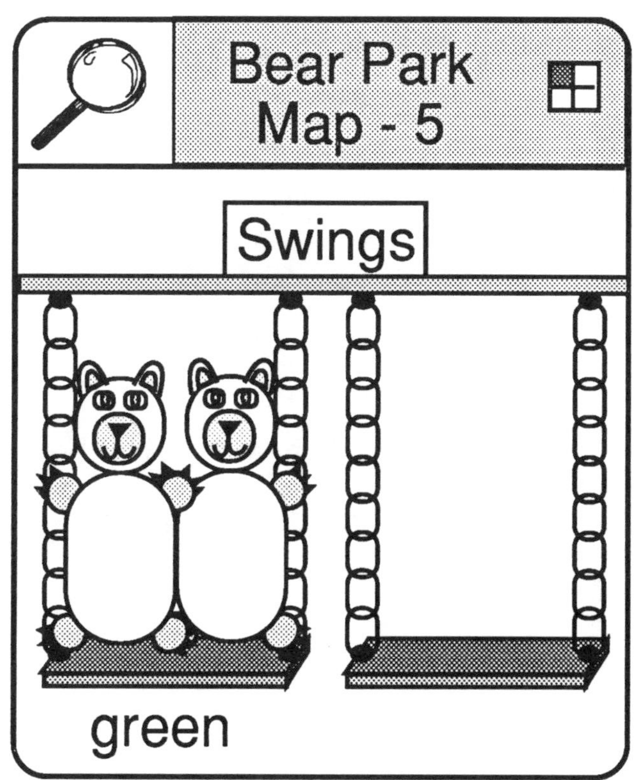

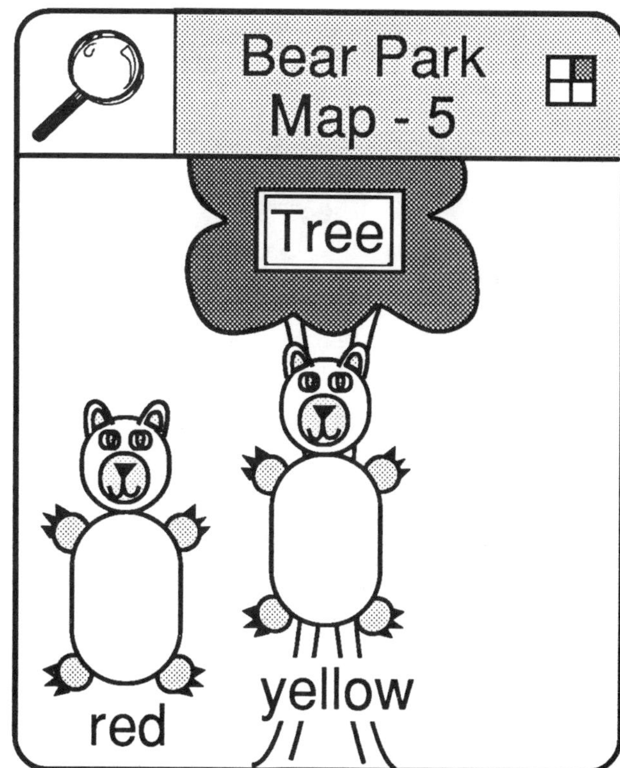

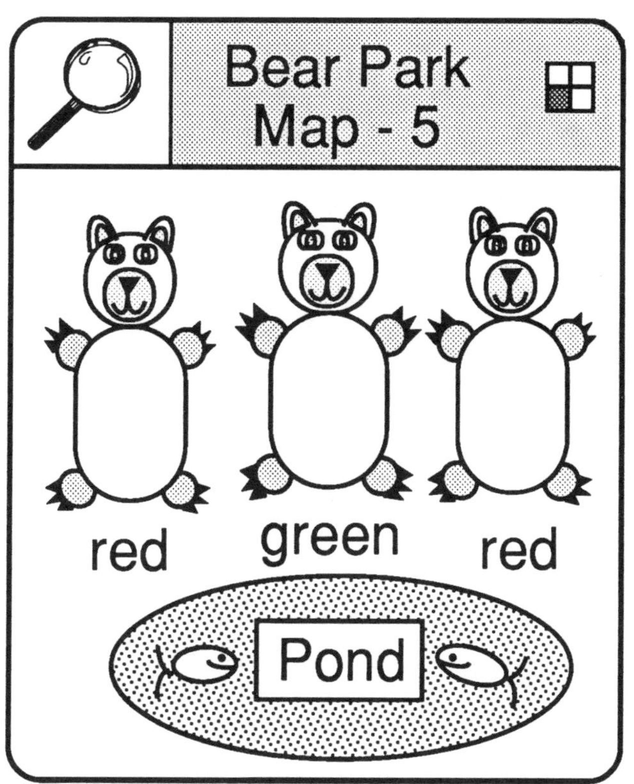

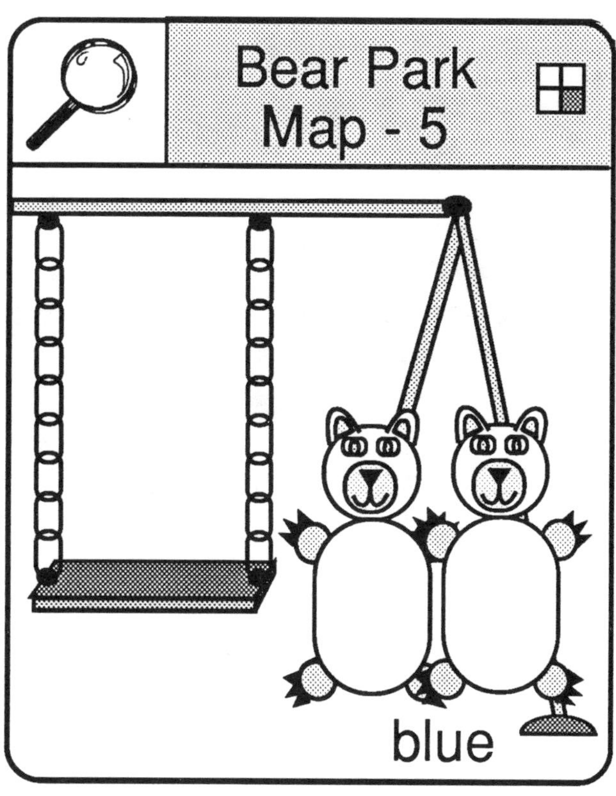

TEACHER NOTES: Each group will need a set of clue cards; one Bear Park map; and at least four bears in each of the following colors: red, blue, yellow and green. Explain to the students that they will use all four clues to place the bears on the map. Encourage students to place the bears as accurately as they can.

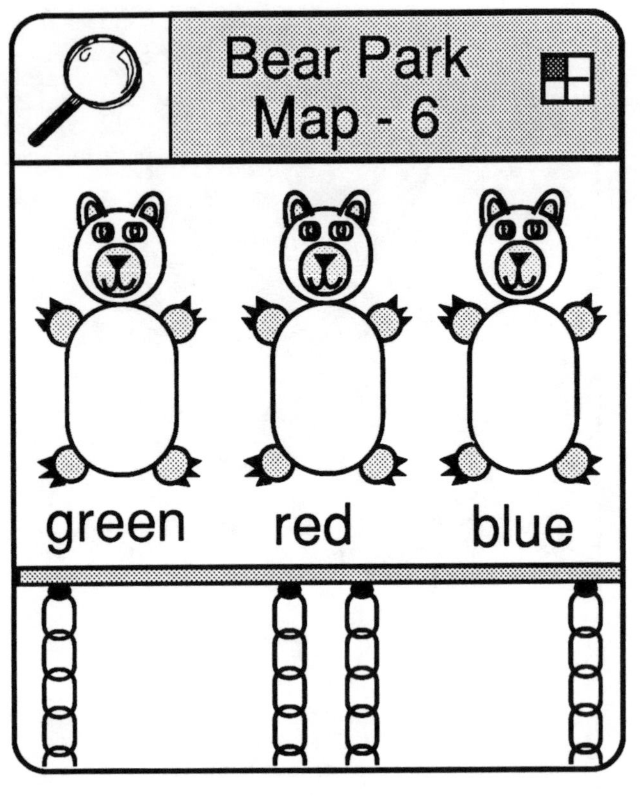

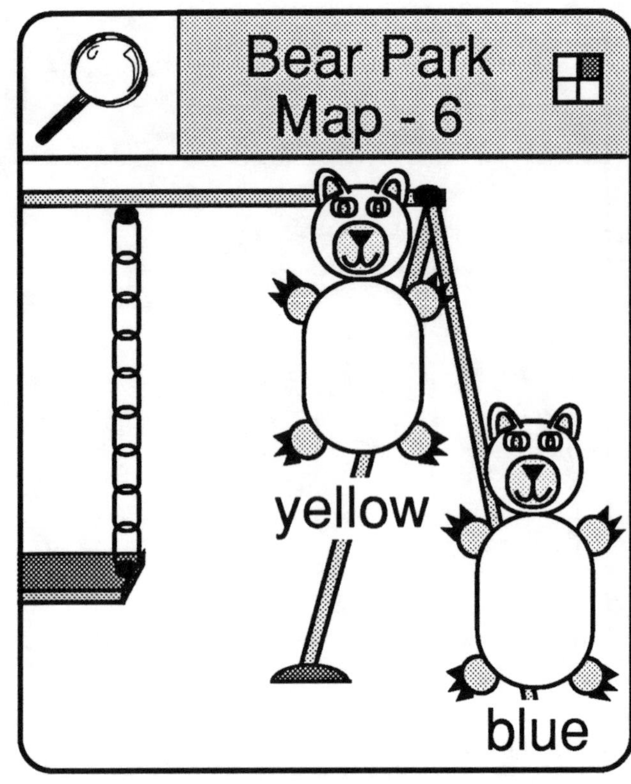

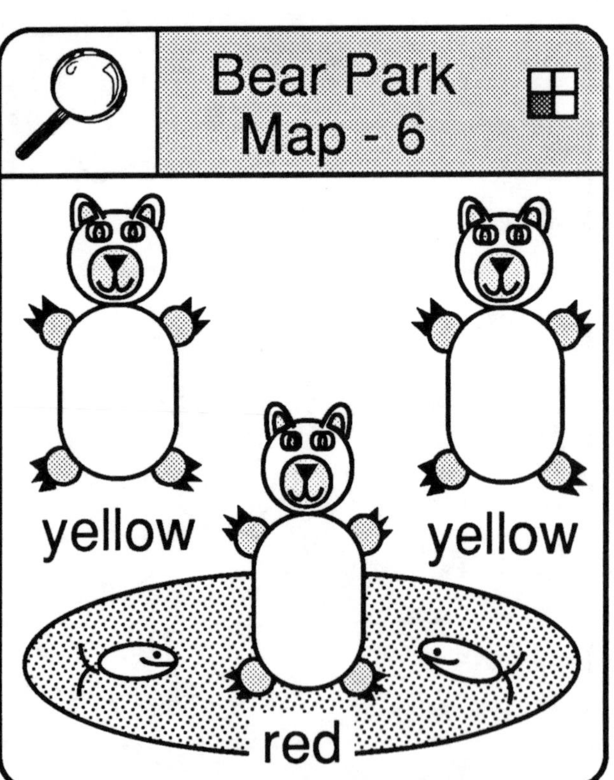

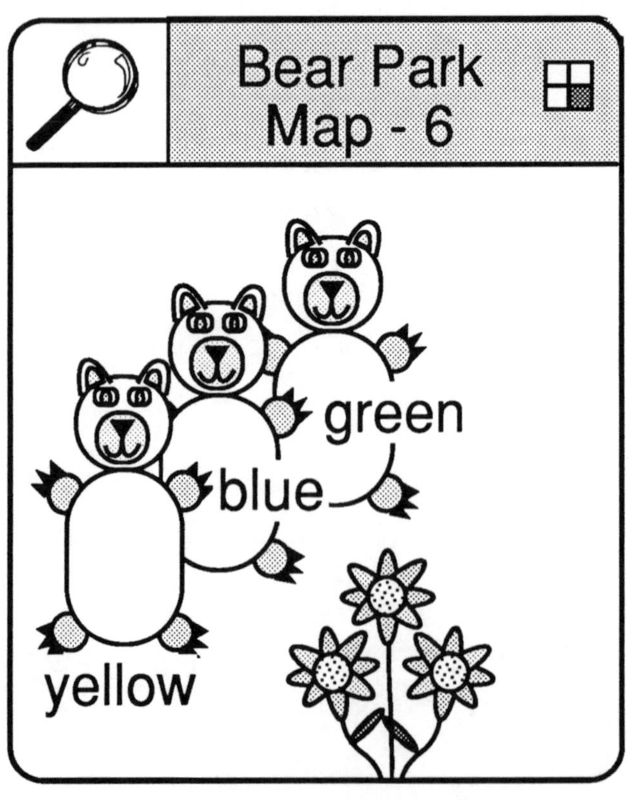

TEACHER NOTES: Each group will need a set of clue cards; one Bear Park map; and at least four bears in each of the following colors: red, blue, yellow and green. Explain to the students that they will use all four clues to place the bears on the map. Encourage students to place the bears as accurately as they can.

Bear Park
Map - 7

Put 2 red bears on 1 swing.

Bear Park
Map - 7

Put 3 green bears in the pond.

Bear Park
Map -7

Put 3 yellow bears by the tree.

Bear Park
Map - 7

Put 1 blue bear by the flowers.

 TEACHER NOTES: Each group will need a set of clue cards; one Bear Park map; and at least four bears in each of the following colors: red, blue, yellow and green. Explain to the students that they will use all four clues to place the bears on the map.

Bear Park
Map - 8

Put 1 yellow bear and 2 blue bears on top of the swings.

Bear Park
Map - 8

Put 2 yellow bears and 1 green bear by the pond.

Bear Park
Map - 8

Put 1 red bear on the left side of the tree.

Bear Park
Map - 8

Put 2 green bears in the flowers.

TEACHER NOTES: Each group will need a set of clue cards; one Bear Park map; and at least four bears in each of the following colors: red, blue, yellow and green. Explain to the students that they will use all four clues to place the bears on the map.

Bear Street Map
N
W
E
S
Bear
Hill
28
30
26
24
Bear
Pond
20
22

Bear Street Map - 1

A blue bear lives in the house with the highest number.

Bear Street Map - 1

A red bear lives in the house next to Bear Pond.

Bear Street Map - 1

A yellow bear lives in the house next to the Bear Hill.

Bear Street Map - 1

Green bears live in three houses.

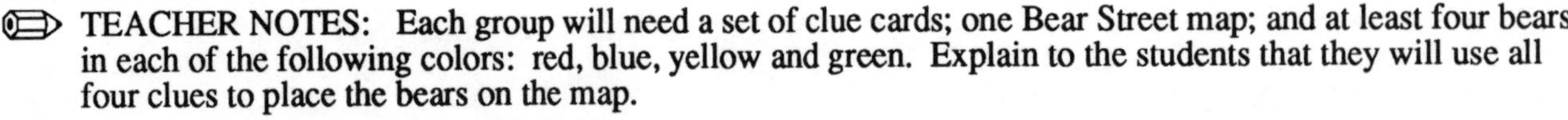

TEACHER NOTES: Each group will need a set of clue cards; one Bear Street map; and at least four bears in each of the following colors: red, blue, yellow and green. Explain to the students that they will use all four clues to place the bears on the map.

Bear Street
Map - 2

A yellow bear lives in the house next to Bear Hill. The other yellow bear lives next door to the blue bear.

Bear Street
Map - 2

The red bear lives in the house that is just below 26 Bear Street.

Bear Street
Map - 2

The green bear's house is between two flowers.

Bear Street
Map - 2

A blue bear lives in the house that is just above 22 Bear Street. No bears live at 30 Bear Street.

 TEACHER NOTES: Each group will need a set of clue cards; one Bear Street map; and at least four bears in each of the following colors: red, blue, yellow and green. Explain to the students that they will use all four clues to place the bears on the map.

Bear Street Map - 3

A blue bear and a yellow bear live in the houses on the south part of the map. The yellow bear lives closest to the pond.

Bear Street Map - 3

A red bear can go just outside her house to climb a tree.

Bear Street Map - 3

Green bears live in the two houses that are just east of Bear Hill.

Bear Street Map - 3

A blue bear lives in a house that is north of 20 Bear Street.

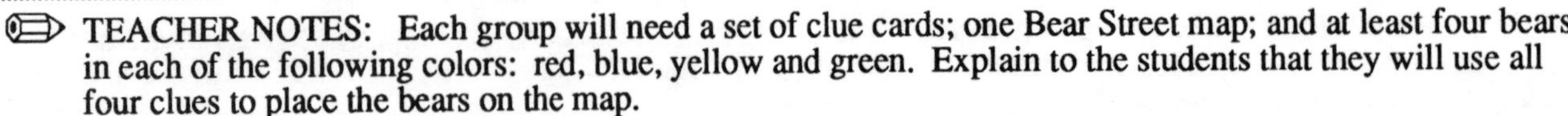

TEACHER NOTES: Each group will need a set of clue cards; one Bear Street map; and at least four bears in each of the following colors: red, blue, yellow and green. Explain to the students that they will use all four clues to place the bears on the map.

Bear Street Map - 4

All the bears live in pairs. Two of the pairs are red.

Bear Street Map - 4

Two houses are east of Bear Pond. A blue bear and a yellow bear live in each of these houses.

Bear Street Map - 4

A blue bear and a green bear live in the house that is just north of the tree.

Bear Street Map - 4

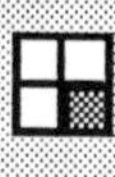

A yellow bear lives with a red bear. The bears who live next door are blue and green.

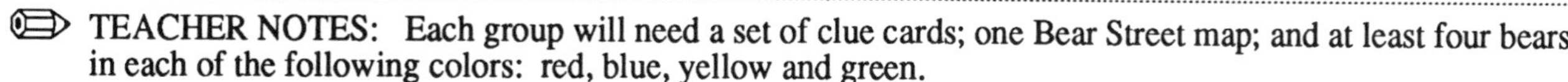

TEACHER NOTES: Each group will need a set of clue cards; one Bear Street map; and at least four bears in each of the following colors: red, blue, yellow and green.

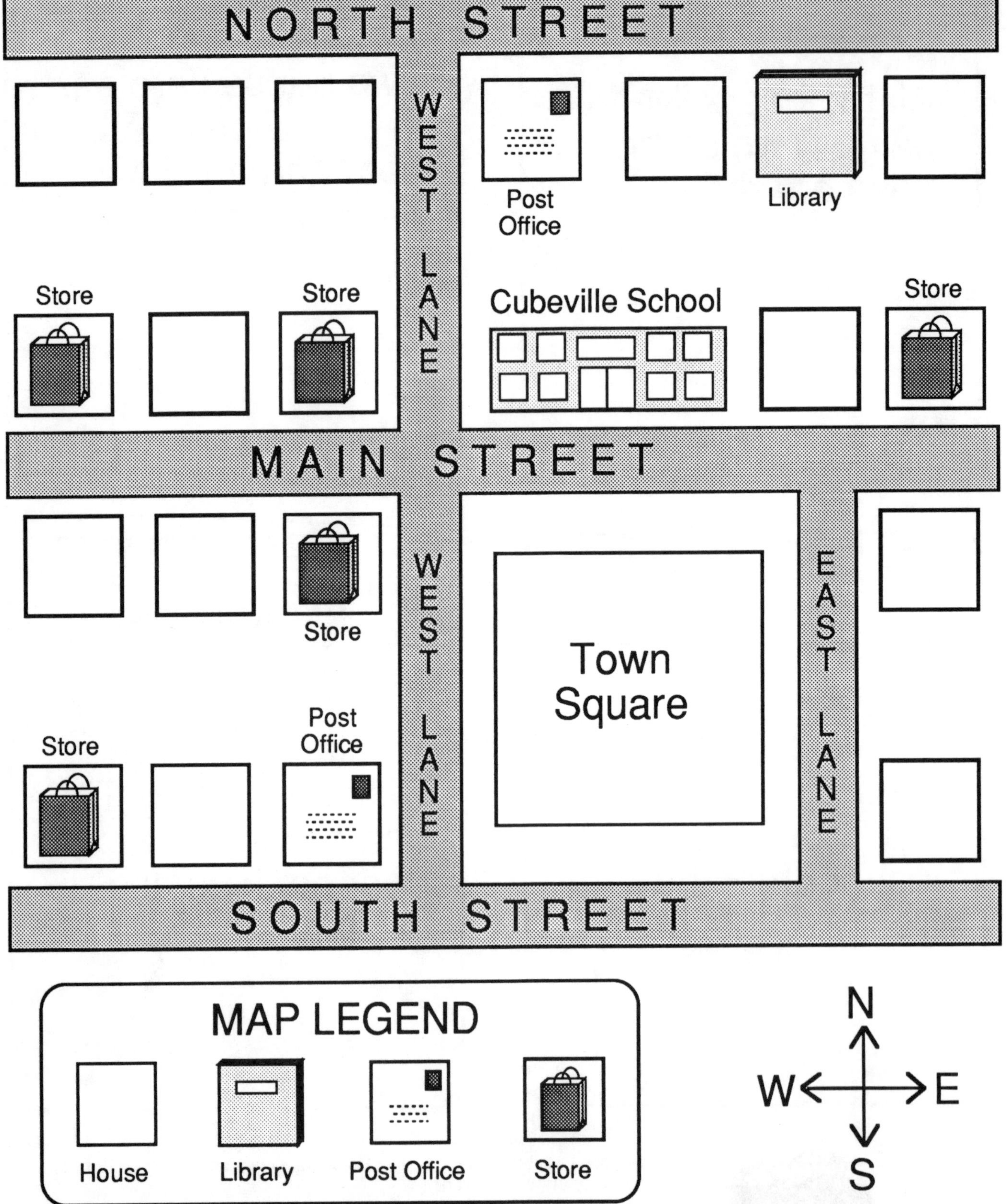
Cubeville Map
NORTH STREET
WEST LANE
Post Office
Library
Store
Store
Cubeville School
Store
MAIN STREET
Store
WEST LANE
Town Square
EAST LANE
Post Office
Store
SOUTH STREET
MAP LEGEND
House
Library
Post Office
Store
N
W
E
S

Cubeville Map - 1 

All of the stores in Cubeville are red.

Put the cubes on the map.

Cubeville Map - 1 

The library in Cubeville is blue.

Put the cubes on the map.

Cubeville Map - 1

The post offices in Cubeville are yellow.

Put the cubes on the map.

Cubeville Map - 1 

All of the houses on North Street are green.

Put the cubes on the map.

Cubeville Map - 1

The five houses on Main Street are yellow.

Put the cubes on the map.

Cubeville Map - 1 

All of the houses on South Street are orange.

Put the cubes on the map.

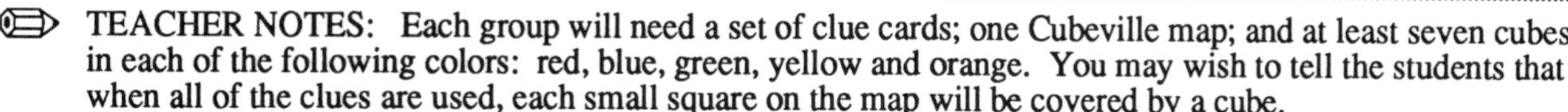

TEACHER NOTES: Each group will need a set of clue cards; one Cubeville map; and at least seven cubes in each of the following colors: red, blue, green, yellow and orange. You may wish to tell the students that when all of the clues are used, each small square on the map will be covered by a cube.

Cubeville Map - 2

There are three orange stores that are north of Main Street. All the other stores are yellow.

Put the cubes on the map.

Cubeville Map - 2

The post office on the corner of West Lane and South Street is blue. The other post office is red.

Put the cubes on the map.

Cubeville Map - 2

There are 5 yellow houses on the street that has the library. The library is red.

Put the cubes on the map.

Cubeville Map - 2

The house next to the Cubeville School is green.

Put the cubes on the map.

Cubeville Map - 2

All of the houses on East Lane are blue.

Put the cubes on the map.

Cubeville Map - 2

There are five green houses in Cubeville.

Put the cubes on the map.

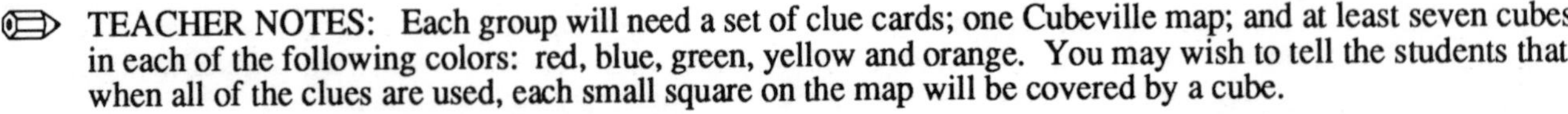

TEACHER NOTES: Each group will need a set of clue cards; one Cubeville map; and at least seven cubes in each of the following colors: red, blue, green, yellow and orange. You may wish to tell the students that when all of the clues are used, each small square on the map will be covered by a cube.

Cubeville Map - 3

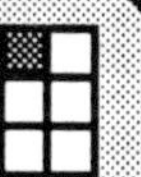

A blue house and an orange store are just east of the Cubeville School.

Put the cubes on the map.

Cubeville Map - 3

On North Street, four buildings are yellow, and three are green. No building is next to a building that is the same color.

Put the cubes on the map.

Cubeville Map - 3

There are three yellow houses on Main Street.

Put the cubes on the map.

Cubeville Map - 3

An orange house is between two red stores on Main Street.

Put the cubes on the map.

Cubeville Map - 3

One post office in Cubeville is blue.

Put the cubes on the map.

Cubeville Map - 3

There are three orange houses and four red stores in Cubeville.

Put the cubes on the map.

TEACHER NOTES: Each group will need a set of clue cards; one Cubeville map; and at least seven cubes in each of the following colors: red, blue, green, yellow and orange. You may wish to tell the students that when all of the clues are used, each small square on the map will be covered by a cube.

Cubeville Map - 4

One street in Cubeville has three green houses in a row. One post office is yellow.

Put the cubes on the map.

Cubeville Map - 4

The two houses in Cubeville that are farthest south are blue.

Put the cubes on the map.

Cubeville Map - 4

A blue house is between the red post office and the orange library.

Put the cubes on the map.

Cubeville Map - 4

One house on East Lane is orange. A green store is north of the house.

Put the cubes on the map.

Cubeville Map - 4

The stores on the corner of Main Street and West Lane are orange.

Put the cubes on the map.

Cubeville Map - 4

There are five red houses in Cubeville. There are two blue stores in Cubeville.

Put the cubes on the map.

 TEACHER NOTES: Each group will need a set of clue cards; one Cubeville map; and at least seven cubes in each of the following colors: red, blue, green, yellow and orange. You may wish to tell the students that when all of the clues are used, each small square on the map will be covered by a cube.

Graph Paper (for Cubeville Maps)

TEACHER NOTES: If you do not have wood cubes in your classroom, duplicate this page on red, yellow, blue, green and orange paper. The paper squares can be placed on the Cubeville map.

➤*Sources for Materials*◄

COINS

Coins are used with all **Coin Count** activities. Sets of coins (30 pennies, 20 nickels, 20 dimes, 20 quarters, 4 half dollars). One set of coins can be shared by two groups of four students. Coin Stamps are optional and can be used to record solutions or to create your own cooperative logic problems.

These materials are available from:

CUISINAIRE COMPANY OF AMERICA
P.O. Box 5026
White Plains, NY 10602-5026

1-800-237-3142 (telephone)
1-800-551-RODS (fax)

Ordering information and prices are:

031090 Coins (one set - 94 pieces) $5.50
029060 Set of 5 Coin Stamps (heads) $8.95
029061 Set of 5 Coin Stamps (tails) $8.95

HUNDRED CHARTS

The Hundred Chart is used with **Secret Number** activities. The large wall chart is an optional tool to record the process of elimination with the whole class. Laminated hundred number boards can be used to record each group's solution with wipe-off pens and will save paper.

These materials are available from:

CUISINAIRE COMPANY OF AMERICA
P.O. Box 5026
White Plains, NY 10602-5026

1-800-237-3142 (telephone)
1-800-551-RODS (fax)

Ordering information and prices are:

010459 Hundred Number Wall Chart $16.95
010463 Hundred Number Boards (set of 10) $7.95

Hundred Chart

1	2	3	4	5	6	7	8	9	10
11	12	13	14	15	16	17	18	19	20
21	22	23	24	25	26	27	28	29	30
31	32	33	34	35	36	37	38	39	40
41	42	43	44	45	46	47	48	49	50
51	52	53	54	55	56	57	58	59	60
61	62	63	64	65	66	67	68	69	70
71	72	73	74	75	76	77	78	79	80
81	82	83	84	85	86	87	88	89	90
91	92	93	94	95	96	97	98	99	100

TEDDY BEAR COUNTERS

Teddy bear counters are used with **Bear Line-Ups, Bear Park Maps** and **Bear Street Maps**. A bucket of 300 bears is ample for a classroom of 35 students.

The bears are available from:

ETA
620 Lakeview Parkway
Vernon Hills, IL 60061

1-800-445-5985 (telephone)
1-708-816-5066 (fax)

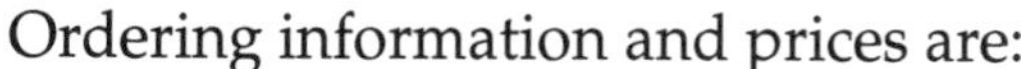

Ordering information and prices are:

926-M3 Baby Bears in 4 colors, set of 100 $10.95
951-M3 Baby Bears in 4 colors, set of 300 $31.95

WOOD CUBES

Wood cubes are used with **Cubeville Maps**. They are available in bags of six assorted colors (red, blue, green, yellow, orange, white). One bag has enough cubes for two groups of four students.

Cubes are available from:

TEACHING RESOURCE CENTER
PO Box 1509
14023 Catalina Street
San Leandro, CA 94577

1-800-833-3389 (telephone)
1-800-972-7722 (fax)

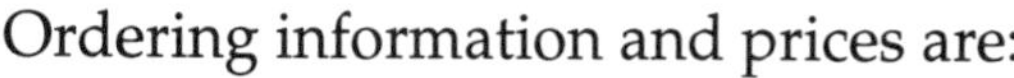

Ordering information and prices are:

93-ER-04 2 cm Colored Cubes (bag of 100) $10.95

➤Activity Grid: Grade Levels◄

SEARCHES

Activity	Suggested Grade Levels					
	K	1	2	3	4	5
Find The House	✓	✓	✓			
Find The Animal	✓	✓	✓			
Find The Monkey	✓	✓	✓			
Find The Pet Shop	✓	✓	✓	✓		
Find The Bear		✓	✓	✓		
Find Rosa's Robot			✓	✓	✓	
Find The Pizza—1			✓	✓	✓	
Find The Pizza—2				✓	✓	
Pizza Match—1 and 2					✓	✓

BEAR LINE-UPS

Activity	Suggested Grade Levels					
	K	1	2	3	4	5
Bear Line-Up 1–4	✓	✓	✓			
Bear Line-Up 5		✓	✓			
Bear Line-Up 6 and 7			✓	✓		
Bear Line-Up 8 and 9			✓	✓	✓	
Bear Line-Up 10 and 11				✓	✓	✓

SECRET NUMBER

	Suggested Grade Levels					
Activity	K	1	2	3	4	5
Secret Number A–C			✓	✓	✓	
Secret Number D				✓	✓	
Secret Number E–H				✓	✓	✓

COIN COUNT

	Suggested Grade Levels					
Activity	K	1	2	3	4	5
Coin Count 1–5	✓	✓	✓			
Coin Count 6		✓	✓			
Coin Count 7			✓	✓		
Coin Count 8			✓	✓	✓	
Coin Count 9 and 10				✓	✓	
Coin Count 11 and 12				✓	✓	✓

MAPS

	Suggested Grade Levels					
Activity	K	1	2	3	4	5
Bear Park 1–6	✓	✓	✓			
Bear Park 7 and 8		✓	✓			
Bear Street 1 and 2			✓	✓	✓	
Bear Street 3 and 4				✓	✓	
Cubeville Map 1				✓	✓	
Cubeville Map 2–4					✓	✓

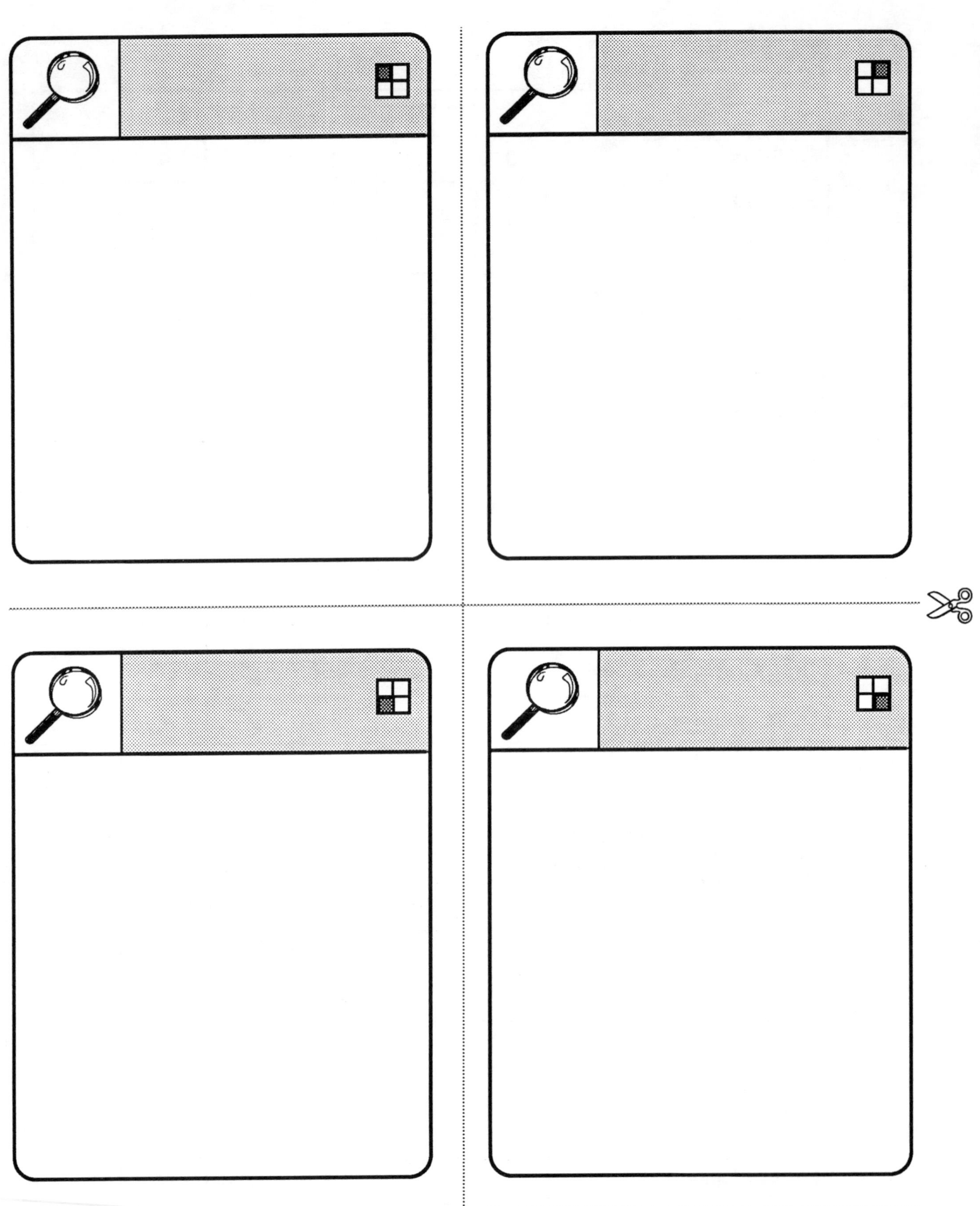

TEACHER NOTES:

TEACHER NOTES:

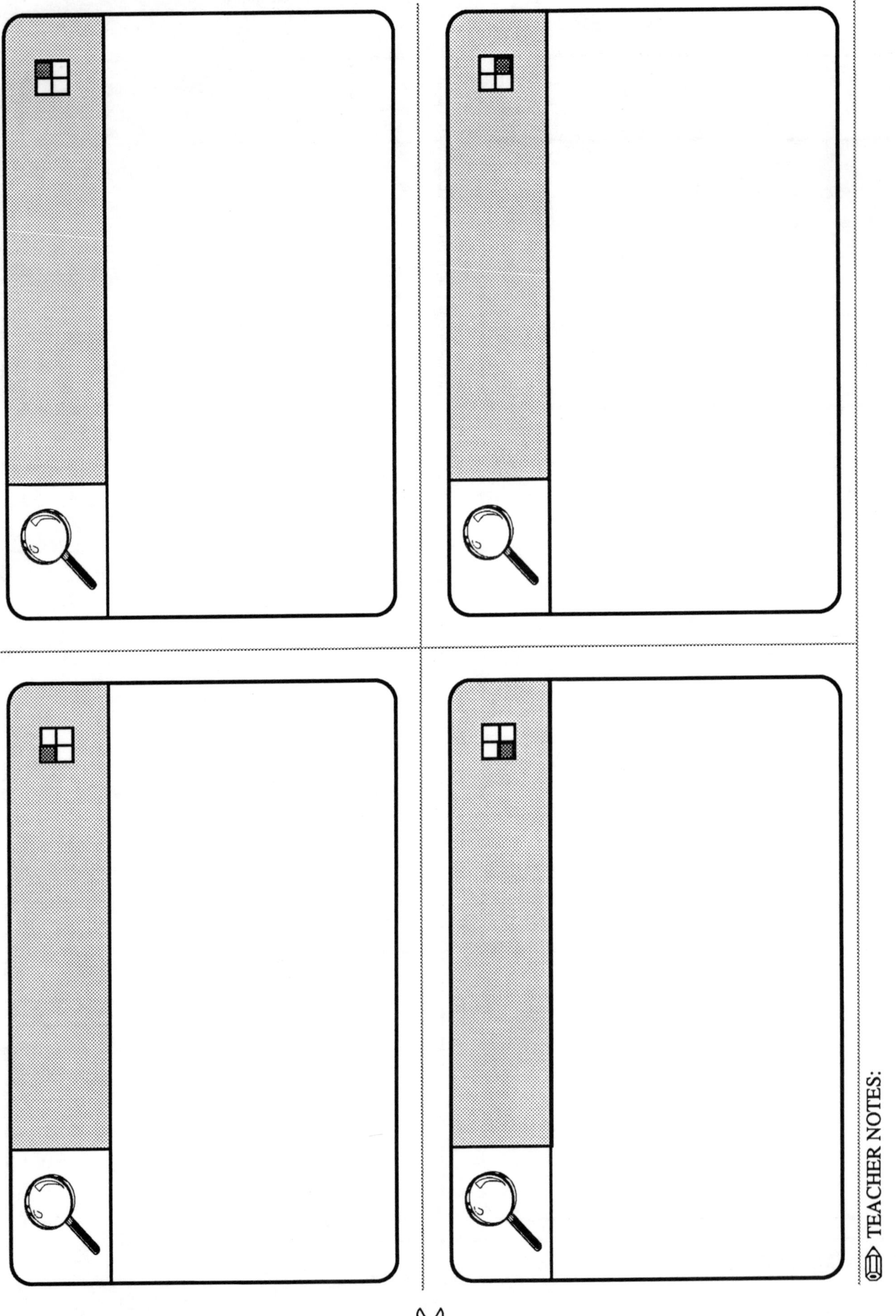

TEACHER NOTES:

Get Connected!
www.lhs.berkeley.edu/GEMS

Get Connected!

Get the *GEMS Network News*

our free educational newsletter filled with—

Updates on GEMS activities and publications.
Suggestions from GEMS enthusiasts around the country.
Strategies to help you and your students succeed.
Information about workshops and leadership training.
Announcements of new publications and resources.

Be part of a growing national network of people who are committed to activity-based science and math education. Stay connected with the GEMS Network News. If you don't already receive the Network News, simply return the attached postage-paid card.

For more information about GEMS call (510) 642-7771, or write to GEMS, Lawrence Hall of Science, University of California, Berkeley, California 94720-5200.

GEMS activities are easy-to-use and effective. They engage students in cooperative, hands-on science and math explorations, while introducing key principles and concepts.

More than 60 GEMS Teacher's Guides and Handbooks have been developed at the Lawrence Hall of Science-the Public science center at the University of California Berkeley–and tested in thousands of classrooms nationwide. There are many more to come–along with local GEMS workshops and GEMS centers and Network Sites springing up across the nation to provide support, training, and resources for you and your colleagues!

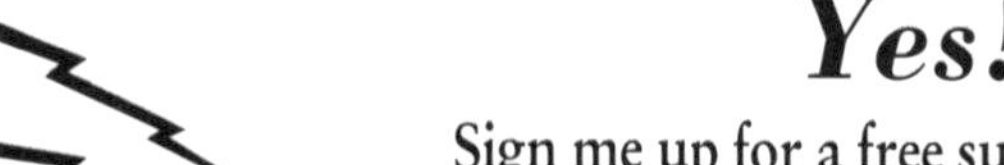

Yes!

Sign me up for a free subscription to the

GEMS Network News

filled with ideas, information, and strategies that lead to Great Explorations in Math and Science!

Name____

Address____

City_______________________ State________Zip___________

How did you find out about GEMS? (Check all that apply.)
❐ word of mouth ❐ conference ❐ ad ❐ workshop ❐ other: ____________________

❐ In addition to the *GEMS Network News,* please send me a free catalog of GEMS materials.

GEMS
Lawrence Hall of Science
University of California
Berkeley, California 94720-5200
(510) 642-7771

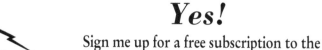

Ideas ◂ *Suggestions* ◂ Resources ◂

Sign up now for a free subscription to the *GEMS Network News!*

that lead to Great Explorations in Math and Science!

LH68
101 Lawrence Hall of Science # 5200

NO POSTAGE
NECESSARY
IF MAILED
IN THE
UNITED STATES

BUSINESS REPLY MAIL
FIRST-CLASS MAIL PERMIT NO. 7 BERKELEY, CA

POSTAGE WILL BE PAID BY THE ADDRESSEE

UNIVERSITY OF CALIFORNIA BERKELEY
GEMS
LAWRENCE HALL OF SCIENCE
PO BOX 16000
BERKELEY CA 94704-9700,

Group Solutions
Casebook

Name ______________________________

✂ -

Group Solutions
Casebook

Name ______________________________

Name of Case____

Write or draw your solution below:

✂ -

Name of Case____

Write or draw your solution below:

➤ How to Make a Group Solutions Kit for Your School ◄

Three elementary schools in Pittsburg, California, created schoolwide kits that contain ten copies of all 57 Group *Solutions* activities. The kits are stored in a central location, along with a copy of *Group Solutions*. Teachers sign out the materials to use with students.

To make a kit, you will need:

- ➤ 570 standard size white envelopes (4.25" X 9.5") — 10 for each activity
- ➤ 63 letter size pocket folders (expandable to 2") — to store 10 envelopes for each activity—and copies of Bear Park, Bear Street, and Cubeville Maps; Coin Count Recording Sheet; and Fifty and Hundred charts.
- ➤ 5 banker's boxes (standard size) — to store the pocket folders for each family of activities
- ➤ 5 reams (250 sheets each) of cardstock (60 lb. weight paper) in several light colors; include at least one ream of white cardstock
- ➤ Medium point markers: four each of red, yellow, blue, green (to color bears on clue cards); and silver and copper/tan (to color coins on clue cards)
- ➤ One ream (500 sheets) of white paper to duplicate Fifty Charts, Hundred Charts, Coin Count Recording Sheets
- ➤ At least one paper cutter, to cut activity sheets

OPTIONAL: 40 sheets of 11" x 17" white paper to duplicate enlarged Bear Park, Bear Street and Cubeville Maps

To create your kit, follow the steps on the next page. Don't take on the project alone! With specific instructions, volunteers can assume responsibility for the following tasks:

- ➤ Duplicate the copies (Step # 1).
- ➤ Color in the clue cards for younger readers (Bear Line-Ups 1-4; Coin Count 1-6); Bear Park Map 3-4). Provide a correctly colored model for the volunteer to use.
- ➤ Write the activity titles on the white envelopes (Step # 2). Have the envelopes ready BEFORE you cut the copies.
- ➤ Cut up the copies and put one set of cards in each labeled envelope.
- ➤ Write the family title on the pocket folders. (Step # 3)

In Pittsburg, the copies were duplicated; envelopes, pocket folders, and markers were bought; paper cutters were mobilized from classrooms; and all materials were gathered in a central area. Teachers set up an assembly line and completed the kit in several hours!

➤*Steps to Create Your Kit*◀

Follow these steps for each family in *Group Solutions*

1

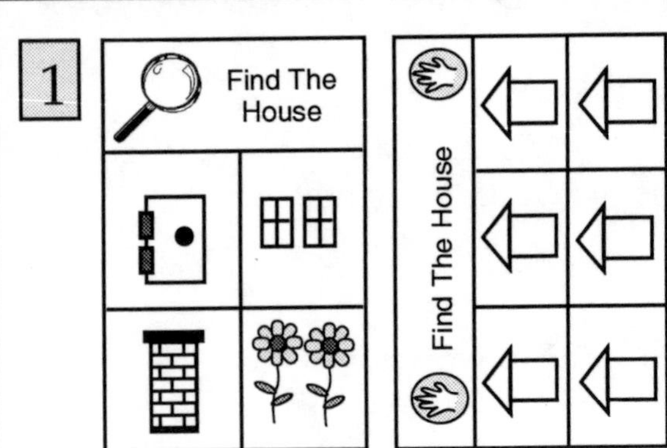

Duplicate 10 copies of each activity on cardstock. Read special instructions in the Getting Ready section and on the bottom of each activity page for preparation suggestions (i.e., when to use white paper and which cards to color).

2

Cut up clue cards and other information (i.e., picture cards in SEARCHES, mats for BEAR LINE-UPS). Place in individual white envelopes. Label the envelope with the name of the activity.

3

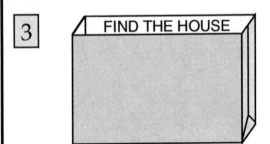

Place the 10 envelopes in a letter-size pocket folder, expandable to two inches. Label the folder. (Extra pocket folders can be used to store Fifty Charts, Hundred Charts, maps & Coin Count Record Sheets.

4

Place the pocket folders in a banker's box. Label the box with the name of the family.
OPTION: Add 10 zip-lock bags or baskets of manipulatives to the box.

NOTE: *After the kit is complete, we suggest you create a sign-out sheet for the activities. Remind teachers to check the envelopes and locate missing pieces before they return the kit. We found the materials stay intact if students NEVER have more than one envelope at a time in their groups.*